M000214280

HIGH SCHOOL

THE INTERNATIONAL SCHOOL OF BEIJING

北京顺义国际学校

School Chemistry Experiments

北京顺义国际学校
THE INTERNATIONAL SCHOOL OF BEIJING

HIGH SCHOOL

A collection of tried and tested experiments for use in schools

Compiled by

Ralph F. Farley
M.Phil., C.Chem., M.R.S.C.,
P.G.Cert.Ed.

Published by:

The Association for Science Education
College Lane
Hatfield
Herts AL10 9AA

Printed by Black Bear Press

Designed and typeset by The Melba Partnership

ISBN 0 86357 326 6

FOREWORD

This is a book of chemistry experiments collected over the past 20 years of teaching 11–18 year-olds in UK schools. There are 17 chapters, 15 of which begin with the context in which the experiments are set. Chapter 16 describes the preparation of the gases needed for the experiments in the book. The last chapter contains information which the practitioner could find useful for setting activities which involve the identification of unknown substances likely to be met in school chemistry lessons.

The details of each experiment begin with a list of the apparatus needed for the experiment. Safety information is next and this is followed by step-by-step instructions on how to carry out the experiment. Sample results follow and the experiment ends with background information together with some tricks of the trade which will ensure that the experiment is successful. There are also, where appropriate, suggestions on how the activity might be extended for the more able and A-level students.

The nomenclature of *Signs, Symbols and Systematics* (ASE, 2000) has been adopted throughout this book.

I have tried to simplify the language as much as possible without detracting from the important points and I believe that I have produced a text that is concise and easy to understand. The experiments have already been trialled for you and the quantities and methods modified to ensure safety and success. If you follow the instructions as written, the experiments work.

I hope you will enjoy doing the experiments and that your students' learning will be greatly enhanced by that experience.

Ralph F. Farley

CONTENTS

v

HEALTH AND SAFETY

I have attempted to identify all the recognised hazards in the practical activities in this text, provided suitable warnings about them and suggested appropriate precautions. The ASE Safeguards Committee's advice has been followed in the writing of the text. It should be remembered, however, that where there is a hazard, the employer is required to carry out a risk assessment under the COSHH Regulations or the Management of Health and Safety at Work Regulations. If there are any doubts about the suitability of any of the experiments in this collection then members should check with the ASE, CLEAPSS School Science Service or, in Scotland, SSERC. Also, check with your employer whether the activity is acceptable.

The practical work should be carried out in a properly equipped and maintained laboratory and good practice observed when carrying out the experiments. Suitable eye protection must be worn whenever the risk assessment requires it. If a demonstration requires the use of safety screens, then they should be designed to protect both the teacher and the students and be tall enough and sufficiently close to the apparatus to prevent objects going over the top. Students should be at least 2 m from the safety screen. Fume cupboards should conform to standards of Building Bulletin 88, *Fume Cupboards in Schools* (Architects and Buildings Branch, DfEE, 1998, HMSO); see also *Topics in Safety* (3rd edition), ASE 2001, Topic 7. If safety screens and fume cupboards are not available, then activities which require them should not be attempted.

The decision as to which age groups the activities are most appropriate for is left to the teacher, taking the employer's risk assessments into account. *Topics in Safety* (ASE, 2001, third edition), *Safety in Science Education* (DfEE, 1996), *Hazcards* (CLEAPSS, 1995 or later), and *Hazardous Chemicals. A manual for science education* (SSERC, 1997), are all useful references for deciding on the approximate age of students for which particular activities are appropriate or whether they are only suitable as a teacher demonstration.

Risk assessments will depend on the nature of the teaching group. What is an acceptable risk with one group may be unacceptable with another. In a few cases, proposed activities may not be covered by the Model (general) Risk Assessments commonly used in school science. In such cases, a special risk assessment may be necessary before the employer can permit the activity to take place.

1 SEPARATION OF MIXTURES

A mixture is a system of two or more substances which are not chemically combined and therefore the components which constitute the mixture retain their individual chemical and physical properties. If the components are equally dispersed throughout, the mixture is homogeneous. If the components are unevenly distributed then the mixture is heterogeneous. The difference in physical properties of the components of the mixture determines the method of separation.

1.1 Decanting

Two beakers (250 cm^3) Spoon spatula
Sand Measuring cylinder (100 cm^3)
Glass rod

Safety Low hazard

Method

1. Put 10 rounded spatula measures of sand in one of the beakers.
2. Add 100 cm^3 of tap water and stir the mixture with the glass rod.
3. Let the sand separate out under gravity and simply pour off the clear supernatant into the empty beaker without disturbing the sediment (see Figure 1.1).

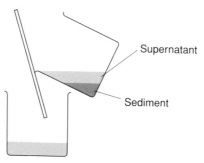

Figure 1.1 Decanting.

Notes

1. This method is suitable for mixtures of high density insoluble solids in liquids.
2. Pouring the supernatant down a glass rod will prevent drips running down from the spout of the beaker.

1.2 Centrifugation

Centrifuge
Centrifuge tubes
Top-pan balance
Dry powdered clay (fuller's earth)
Aluminium sulfate(VI) solution
  ($0.1 \, mol \, dm^{-3}$)

Spoon spatula
Two beakers ($100 \, cm^3$)
Measuring cylinder ($100 \, cm^3$)
Glass rod

Safety Do not use dry clay powder from the art department. It is carcinogenic! Make sure the centrifuge conforms to modern safety standards, e.g. the power goes off when the lid is lifted. Do not open the lid of the centrifuge until it has stopped spinning.

Method

1. Put $50 \, cm^3$ of aluminium sulfate(VI) solution into the beaker and add two rounded spatula measures of clay powder.

2. Stir the mixture with the glass rod.

3. Fill a centrifuge tube with some of the mixture and weigh it.

4. Fill another centrifuge tube with some more of the mixture so that the filled tubes have equal mass.

5. Put the tubes opposite each other in the centrifuge and spin down the solids for two minutes.

6. Remove the tubes from the centrifuge and decant off the supernatant into a clean beaker.

Notes

1. A centrifuge is a device in which a suspension of fine particles in a liquid is separated by rotating at speed in a tube in a horizontal circle. The suspended particles move along the tube to a greater radius of rotation and collect together at the bottom of the tube (see Figure 1.2).

Precipitate

Supernatant

Figure 1.2 Centrifugation.

2. When using a centrifuge, always divide the mixture and use two tubes so that the tubes counterbalance each other from the centre of rotation.

3. The aluminium ions prevent the clay from forming a colloidal suspension.

1.3 Filtration

Conical flask (100 cm³)
Filter funnel
Filter paper
Beaker (100 cm³)
Spoon spatula
Glass rod
Powdered chalk
Measuring cylinder (100 cm³)

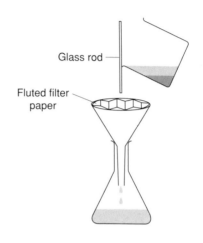

Glass rod

Fluted filter paper

Figure 1.3 Filtration.

Safety Low hazard

Method

1. Put 50 cm³ of tap water into the beaker and add two rounded spatula measures of powdered chalk.

2. Fold a filter-paper disc into a cone, place it in the funnel and put the funnel in the neck of the conical flask.

3. Stir the mixture with the glass rod and pour it down the rod and into the filter-paper cone (see Figure 1.3).

4. Collect the filtrate in the conical flask.

Notes

1. Filtration is the use of semipermeable materials which act like a sieve to separate a solid from a liquid. The particles of the solid are held back while the liquid is able to pass through the material. The most usual filters are discs made from 'blotting paper' and sintered glass crucibles.

2. Filter-paper discs can be used flat with a Buchner funnel and flask connected to a vacuum pump, or folded into a cone and used with a cone-shaped funnel. The filter paper can be folded in half and then into quarters to make the cone, or it can be fluted. Fluted filter paper is preferable because the whole of the paper surface is exposed to the mixture compared with only half of the surface of a folded paper.

1.4 Evaporation

Bunsen burner	Beaker ($100\,cm^3$)
Tripod and gauze	Distilled water
Evaporating basin	Measuring cylinder ($25\,cm^3$)
Sodium chloride	Glass rod
Spoon spatula	Eye protection

Figure 1.4 Evaporation.

Safety When the solution has nearly all evaporated, there is a risk of salt particles spitting out of the basin. Eye protection is essential.

Method
1. Put $25\,cm^3$ of distilled water into the beaker and add one rounded spatula measure of sodium chloride.
2. Stir the mixture with the glass rod until the sodium chloride has dissolved.
3. Pour the solution into the evaporating basin and evaporate to dryness on a tripod and gauze over the Bunsen burner (see Figure 1.4).

Note
Evaporation is the process of separating out a solution of a non-volatile solid from a volatile liquid. When the solution is heated, the liquid turns to vapour and becomes dispersed in the air and the solid is left as a residue in the basin.

1.5 Sublimation

Evaporating basin   Tripod and gauze
Spoon spatula   Ammonium chloride
Glass funnel   Sand
Retort stand and clamp   Eye protection
Bunsen burner

Safety Ammonium chloride fumes cause irritation to eyes, nose
and throat if inhaled. It is harmful if swallowed.

Method

1. Put one rounded spatula measure of ammonium chloride and two of
   sand into the evaporating basin and mix.

2. Put the evaporating basin on the tripod and gauze and hold an
   inverted glass funnel over the evaporating basin with the retort and
   clamp.

3. Heat the mixture in the evaporating basin and collect the sublimate
   on the inverted glass funnel.

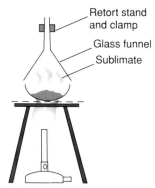

Figure 1.5 Sublimation.

Notes

1. Sublimation is the conversion of a solid into a gas without going
   through the liquid stage. This happens when a solid has a melting
   point and a boiling point close together. Solid mixtures in which one
   component will sublime when heated can be separated in this way.

2. In this experiment, the ammonium chloride sublimed by
   decomposing and then reforming and the sand remained in the
   evaporating basin.

$$NH_4Cl(s) \rightleftharpoons NH_3(g) + HCl(g)$$

1.6 Crystallisation

Copper(II) sulfate(VI)	Forceps
Distilled water	Bunsen burner
Spoon spatula	Tripod and gauze
Two beakers (250 cm^3)	Plastic bowl
Glass rod	Thermometer
Measuring cylinder (100 cm^3)	Eye protection

Safety Solid copper(II) sulfate(VI) and its aqueous solution ≥ 1 mol dm^{-3} are harmful if swallowed.

Method

1. Put 100 cm^3 of distilled water into a beaker and heat it above room temperature.

2. Add copper(II) sulfate(VI) while stirring until no more will dissolve and stand the beaker in a bowl of cold water.

3. When the mixture is at room temperature, decant the saturated copper(II) sulfate(VI) supernatant solution into another beaker.

4. Seed the saturated solution with one small crystal of copper(II) sulfate(VI) and set aside for about six weeks. The crystal will grow.

Notes

1. Crystallisation involves the evaporation of a volatile liquid from a saturated solution of non-volatile solid at room temperature. Bigger and better formed crystals are produced if the process is slow.

2. This process will produce crystals of 5 cm or more in length.

1.7 Distillation

Apparatus as shown in Figure 1.6 on the next page.

Safety Low hazard but eye protection should be worn.

Method

1. Half fill the round-bottomed distillation flask with ink.

2. Add a few anti-bumping granules.

3. Heat the round-bottomed flask gently and collect the distillate in the beaker.

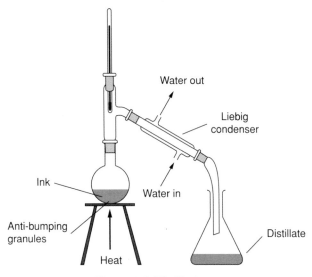

Figure 1.6 Distillation.

Note

Distillation is used for the separation of miscible liquid mixtures in which the components have different boiling points. When the mixture is heated, the component which has the lower boiling point vaporises first.

1.8 Funnel separation

Separating funnel (100 cm³)
Retort stand and clamp
Tap water
Cooking oil
Two beakers (100 cm³)

Safety Low hazard

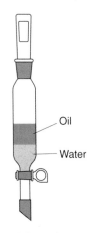

Figure 1.7 Funnel separation.

Method

1. Put 25 cm³ of cooking oil in the separating funnel and add 25 cm³ of tap water.

2. Stopper the funnel and shake it vigorously to mix the oil and water.

3. Hold the funnel in a clamp and stand and let the phases separate.

4. Remove the stopper and run off the lower phase into a beaker.

3. Close the tap when the partition between the two liquids appears in the tap channel.

4. Change beakers and run out a little more liquid until the partition has been expelled. Discard this sample.

7. Run off the remaining phase into another clean beaker.

Note

This method is used to separate mixtures of immiscible liquids. The more dense liquid collects at the lower part of the funnel. The less dense liquid collects on top of the more dense liquid and there is a partition between the two.

1.9 Paper chromatography

Gas jar   Paper clip
Glass rod   Distilled water
Pencil   Chromatography paper
Ruler   Scissors
Felt-tip pens containing   Hot-air blower
    water-soluble ink   Measuring cylinder (25 cm³)

Safety If a domestic hair drier has to be used, make sure that it has undergone a portable electrical appliance test and that it is electrically safe.

Method

1. Take a 10 cm length of chromatography paper and draw a pencil line 2 cm from one end.

2. Place a tiny spot of ink from different coloured felt-tip pens on the pencil line and dry them with the hot-air blower.

3. Go over each spot again twice more with the same coloured pen which made the spots and dry the spots with the hot-air blower after each application.

4. Put 25 cm³ of distilled water in the gas jar.

5. Using a paper clip, hang the chromatography paper on a glass rod which has been supported, horizontally, on top of the gas jar so that the edge below the spots is just underneath the surface of the water (see Figure 1.8). Do not immerse the spots!

6. Leave for 10 minutes. The dyes which make up the different coloured inks will separate as the water carries them up the paper.

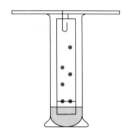

Figure 1.8 Paper chromatography.

Note

Chromatography paper is fine quality 'blotting paper'. Liquids and dissolved solids ascend the 'blotting paper' by capillary flow. The components of the mixture have different flow rates according to the different extents to which they are adsorbed by the paper.

1.10 Mechanical analysis of soil

Hydrogen peroxide (20 vol)
Aqueous sodium   polytrioxo-
    phosphate(V) (5% Calgon)
Measuring cylinders (10, 250 and
    500 cm³)
Top-pan balance
Spatula
Air-dried soil (<2mm)
Beaker (400 cm³)
Glass rod
Cling film

Thermometer
Pipette (25 cm³)
Pipette filler
Evaporating basin
Ruler
Marker pen
Bunsen burner
Tripod and gauze
Distilled water
Rubber tubing connected to a water tap
Eye protection

Safety 20 vol hydrogen peroxide is irritant. Wash hands after handling soil. DO NOT mouth pipette – use the filler.

Method

1. Weigh out 5 g of soil and transfer it to a 400 cm³ beaker.

2. Add 50 cm³ of hydrogen peroxide and heat gently on a tripod and gauze over a Bunsen burner.

3. When frothing ceases, add 150 cm³ of distilled water followed by 10 cm³ of Calgon, stir with a glass rod and leave to stand overnight.

4. Quantitatively transfer to a 500 cm³ measuring cylinder and make the volume up to 500 cm³ with water.

5. Cover the top of the cylinder with cling film to avoid contact with the chemicals. Hold the cling film in place with the palm of the hand and invert a few times to mix. Measure the temperature of the mixture.

6. Mark a 25 cm³ pipette 15 cm from the tip. Mix the soil suspension again and gently place the pipette into the suspension to the 15 cm mark.

7. Using the safety filler, withdraw 25 cm³ samples after the appropriate time has lapsed (see table and Note 4):

Temp./°C	Time/s	Temp./°C	Time/s
10	91.25	22	64.87
12	86.33	24	62.34
14	81.63	26	60.00
16	76.92	28	57.55
18	72.07	30	55.17
20	68.16	32	53.10

8. Transfer the sample to a previously weighed evaporating basin and evaporate to dryness. Find the mass of the residue which is silt + clay.

9. Leave the suspension to stand overnight and, without disturbing the suspension too much, withdraw another 25 cm³ sample and transfer it to another previously weighed evaporating basin. Evaporate to dryness and find the mass of the residue. This is clay.

10. Find the mass of silt by subtraction and calculate the percentage of silt and clay in the soil.

11. Decant and discard the supernatant and quantitatively transfer the sediment to a 400 cm³ beaker.

12. Wash the sediment with a continuous gentle flow of tap water through a rubber tube, the end of which is immersed in the sediment. Continue washing until the supernatant is clear.

13. Decant and discard the supernatant and warm the residue in the beaker over a Bunsen burner until dry. Find the mass of the sediment. This is sand.

14. Calculate the percentage of sand in the soil.

15. Use the soil-texture map (Figure 1.9) to classify the soil according to its texture.

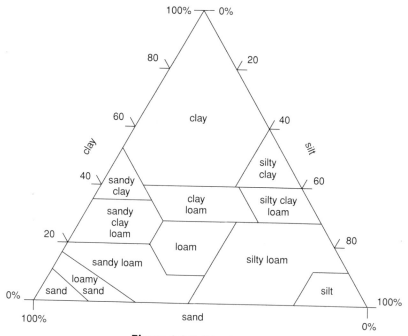

Figure 1.9 Soil texture map.

Sample results

Mass of basin = 43.60 g
Mass of basin + silt + clay = 43.72 g
Mass of silt + clay = 0.12 g
Mass of basin = 45.34 g
Mass of basin + clay = 45.40 g
Mass of clay = 0.06 g
Mass of silt = 0.06 g
Mass of sand = 2.25 g

Calculations

Percentage silt = $500 \div 25 \times 0.06 \times 100 \div 5 = 24\%$

Percentage clay = $500 \div 25 \times 0.06 \times 100 \div 5 = 24\%$

Percentage sand = $2.25 \div 5 \times 100 = 45\%$

Notes

1. The soil was a clay loam.

2. Boiling the soil with hydrogen peroxide oxidises the soil organic matter to carbon dioxide.

3. Calgon complexes calcium and suspends the clay as a colloid.

4. After mixing the suspension prior to withdrawing the sample of silt + clay, the silt and sand particles begin to sink. The velocity with which they sink is proportional to the viscosity of the medium in which they are sinking. The viscosity changes with temperature. The time for the particles to sink 15 cm at different temperatures has been calculated using Stokes' Law.

2 PARTICLES

All matter is made up of tiny particles. In gases the particles are a large distance apart compared to their actual size. There are frequent collisions between the particles which cause them to be in constant random motion, the direction of which changes after each collision. The path followed by a particular particle is a succession of zigzag steps called a 'random walk'. The collisions are elastic so the kinetic energy of the particles does not change and they move with speeds of up to $500\,m\,s^{-1}$.

Diffusion is a fundamental property of all gases. Diffusion is the process by which particles spread out uniformly into the space available to them and is evidence for the existence of particles.

The forces which hold particles together (forces of cohesion) are very weak in gases. In liquids, the forces of cohesion are stronger so the particles are much closer together and are moving more slowly, but are still in constant random motion. In solids, the forces of cohesion are much stronger still and hold the particles in a fixed position. In this state the particles are only able to vibrate about their fixed position. In crystalline solids, there is an orderly arrangement of particles.

2.1 Diffusion of bromine in air

Teat pipette (dropper)   Large white piece of paper
Protective gloves   Ice-cream tub
Bromine   Access to a fume cupboard
Two gas jars (one with a lid)   Eye protection

Safety Bromine vapour is very toxic and the liquid causes severe burns to eyes and skin. Protective gloves are essential and goggles must be worn. The experiment must be done in a fume cupboard. Have a bottle of $1\,mol\,dm^{-3}$ sodium thiosulfate available to treat any spillage.

Method

1. Using the pipette dropper, transfer five drops of bromine to the gas jar and close the jar with the lid.

2. Put the gas jar of bromine in the ice-cream tub containing warm tap water in order to vaporise the bromine.

3. When the gas jar is full of bromine vapour, remove it from the warm water and place it in front of the sheet of white paper.

4. Remove the lid from the gas jar and stand an inverted gas jar containing air on top of the gas jar of bromine vapour.

Sample results

The bromine vapour and air slowly mix until the density of colour is the same in both gas jars. This takes about 1 hour.

Note

Diffusion is the process by which a substance spreads out uniformly throughout the space available to it.

2.2 Diffusion of hydrogen and carbon dioxide in air

Three gas jars containing hydrogen (see Chapter 16)

Three gas jars containing carbon dioxide (see Chapter 16)

Four gas jars containing air

Limewater (saturated aqueous solution of $Ca(OH)_2$)

Wooden splints

Eye protection

Safety Hydrogen–air mixtures are explosive.

Method

1. Show the test for hydrogen by putting a burning splint in one of the gas jars containing hydrogen.

2. Carry out the same test on two gas jars containing air to show the absence of hydrogen in those jars.

3. Take those gas jars of air and invert a gas jar containing hydrogen on one and invert another gas jar of air over the other gas jar of hydrogen.

4. Repeat the procedure with carbon dioxide. Use limewater to test for carbon dioxide.

5. After 15 minutes test all gas jars in contact with hydrogen for the presence of hydrogen and all gas jars in contact with carbon dioxide for the presence of carbon dioxide.

Sample results

All gas jars in contact with hydrogen contained hydrogen and all gas jars in contact with carbon dioxide contained carbon dioxide.

Note

The results show that air and both gases diffused in all directions irrespective of their densities.

2.3 Diffusion of hydrogen and carbon dioxide through a porous pot containing air

Two porous pots fitted with bungs and delivery tubes, one with a U-tube, the other with a double bend

Gas jar containing hydrogen (see Chapter 16)

Gas jar containing carbon dioxide (see Chapter 16)

Very dilute aqueous potassium manganate(VII)

Two retort stands and clamps

Eye protection

Safety Hydrogen–air mixtures are explosive.

Method

1. Put the potassium manganate(VII) solution in the delivery tubes.

2. Support the porous pots by their delivery tubes in the clamps and stands.

3. Invert the gas jar containing hydrogen over the porous pot connected to the U-tube and bring the gas jar of carbon dioxide up underneath the porous pot connected to the double-bend delivery tube (see Figure 2.1).

4. Observe the liquid in the delivery tubes.

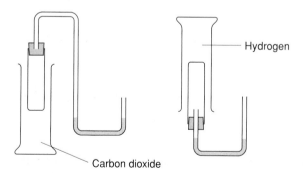

Figure 2.1 Diffusion of gases through porous pots.

Sample results

1. Porous pot in hydrogen: Liquid in the delivery tube moved away from the porous pot because hydrogen diffuses in faster than air diffuses out.

15

2. Porous pot in carbon dioxide: Liquid in the delivery tube moved towards the porous pot, because carbon dioxide diffuses in slower than air in the porous pot diffuses out.

2.4 Diffusion of ammonia and hydrogen chloride in a large glass tube containing air

Large-bore glass tube $(100 \times 2.5\,cm)$ with both ends closed with rubber bungs
Concentrated hydrochloric acid
Concentrated ammonia solution
Cottonwool

Forceps
Universal indicator paper
Metre rule
Two retort stands and clamps
Access to a fume cupboard
Eye protection

Safety Concentrated hydrochloric acid and concentrated ammonia solution must be handled in a fume cupboard because they produce vapours which are toxic. Both of the reagents are corrosive so handle with care. Ammonia can cause asthma attacks in susceptible people so carry out the experiment in a well ventilated room.

Method

1. Support the glass tube horizontally by holding it with a clamp and stand at each end.

2. Remove the bungs and place pH indicator paper every 10 cm inside the tube using the metre rule to position them.

3. Hold a piece of cottonwool with forceps, soak it in ammonia solution, place it in one end of the tube and fit the bung.

4. Put a piece of cottonwool soaked in concentrated hydrochloric acid in the other end of the tube and fit the bung.

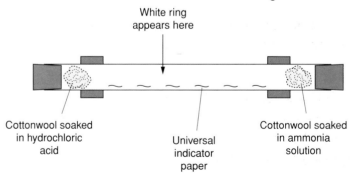

Figure 2.2 Diffusion of hydrogen chloride and ammonia.

5. Observe the apparatus closely over a period of 15 minutes.

Sample results

As the two gases diffused along the inside of the tube towards each other, the pH indicator paper responded appropriately and a white ring appeared one third of the length of the tube from the end containing cottonwool soaked in hydrochloric acid.

Notes

1. The Universal indicator paper turns red in acid, purple in alkali and green when neutral.

2. The white ring was ammonium chloride formed from the reaction between hydrogen chloride and ammonia:

$$NH_3(g) + HCl(g) \rightarrow NH_4Cl(s)$$

Show this reaction to the students by standing the bottles of the reagents next to each other and remove the stoppers. A cloud of white fumes will be seen.

3. The ammonia diffused twice as fast as the hydrogen chloride because the molar mass of ammonia is half the molar mass of hydrogen chloride.

2.5 Diffusion of potassium manganate(VII) in water

Beaker ($250\,cm^3$)   Two measuring cylinders ($100\,cm^3$)
Potassium manganate(VII)   Beaker ($100\,cm^3$)
   (potassium permanganate)   Glass rod
Forceps

Safety **Potassium manganate(VII) is an oxidising agent and harmful. Use forceps to handle the crystals.**

Method

1. Put $100\,cm^3$ of tap water into a $100\,cm^3$ beaker.

2. Using forceps transfer one crystal of potassium manganate(VII) to the water in the beaker.

3. Observe the crystal over a period of 30 minutes.

4. Stir the solution with a glass rod and then make successive dilutions

of 10% in tap water in a 100 cm³ beaker until the colour of the solution is so faint that it is only just visible compared with a similar beaker of water.

5. Count the number of dilutions made.

Sample results

1. The colour of the potassium manganate(VII) slowly spread throughout the water.

2. The resulting solution required five dilutions for the colour to disappear.

Note

The number of dilutions gives an estimate of the number of particles present in the original crystal, i.e. $10 \times 10 \times 10 \times 10 \times 10 = 100\,000$.

2.6 Osmosis

Retort stand and clamp
Sucrose solution (10%) containing
    methylene blue
Test-tube collar fitted with a rubber
    bung and 50 cm of capillary tubing
Beaker (250 cm³)
Dry tea towel
Distilled water
Visking tubing (10 cm)
Toffee hammer, gauze
Emery cloth
Teat pipette (dropper)

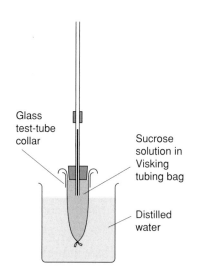

Glass test-tube collar

Sucrose solution in Visking tubing bag

Distilled water

Figure 2.3 Osmosis.

Safety **Prepare the glass collar by wrapping the test-tube in a dry tea towel and break the bottom using the toffee hammer. Using the gauze, chip away the broken test-tube from the bottom until you have the top 1 cm of the tube. Moisten the emery cloth and grind the jagged edge of the test-tube top to a smooth finish. This is best done by holding the emery cloth flat on the bench with one hand and holding the test-tube top between the first finger and thumb of the**

other hand. Make circular movements with the test-tube top whilst applying just enough pressure to keep it in contact with the emery cloth. This must be done in the prep room and not in front of the class. The broken glass is a hazard and goggles must be worn. Dispose of the glass chippings in the 'glass only' waste bin. Do not mix it with other refuse.

Method

1. Soak the Visking tubing in distilled water until it is fully flexible.

2. Make the Visking tubing into a bag by tying a knot in one end and, using a pipette dropper, fill the bag with the sucrose solution containing methylene blue.

3. Using the test-tube top as a sleeve, fix the open end of the Visking tubing to the bung (see Figure 2.3).

4. Immerse the bag of sucrose solution in the beaker of distilled water and support the capillary tube vertically in the clamp and stand.

5. Observe the level of the solution in the capillary tube over a period of 30 minutes.

Sample result

1. The solution in the capillary tube gradually rises.

Notes

1. Osmosis is diffusion through a semipermeable membrane. The particles of water are small enough to diffuse through the walls of the Visking tubing and into the bag but the sucrose particles are too big to pass through and diffuse out. This increases the pressure inside the bag which forces the solution up the capillary tube.

2. The methylene blue makes it easier to see the solution inside the capillary tube.

3. The experiment can be extended by using sucrose solutions of different concentrations inside and outside the bag and comparing the rate of osmosis in terms of how quickly the solution travels up the capillary tube.

2.7 Determination of the concentration of sucrose in potato tissue using osmosis

Three potatoes

Cork borer (6 mm cross-sectional internal diameter)

Sucrose solutions (0.5, 1.0, 1.5, 2.0 and 2.5% w/v)

Measuring cylinder (25 cm³)

Ruler

Scalpel

Absorbent paper tissue

Top-pan balance

Eight boiling tubes, with bungs, in a rack

Forceps

Wooden chopping board

Safety The sharp edges of the cork borer and scalpel should be embedded in corks when not in use.

Method

1. Wash the potatoes under a cold running tap and blot dry with absorbent paper tissue.

2. Put the potatoes on the wooden chopping board and, using the cork borer and scalpel, produce forty potato tuber cylinders, 3 cm³ in length. Remove the skins before cutting to length.

3. Handling the potato cylinders with forceps, put the cylinders in groups of five and weigh them. Calculate and record the average mass.

4. Immerse the groups of five cylinders in 20 cm³ of the sucrose solutions in stoppered boiling tubes for 72 hours at room temperature to reach equilibrium.

5. Using forceps, remove each group of five cylinders from the sucrose solutions, blot them dry with absorbent paper tissue, and re-weigh.

6. Plot a graph of the change in mass/g on the y-axis against concentration of aqueous sucrose in solution/%.

7. Read off the x-axis the concentration of sucrose which corresponds to zero change in mass.

Sample results

Conc. of sucrose/%	Initial mass/g	Final mass/g	(Final − initial mass)/g
0	2.50	3.37	+0.87
0.5	2.37	2.87	+0.50
1.0	2.44	2.59	+0.15
1.5	2.52	2.12	− 0.40
2.0	2.48	2.03	− 0.45
2.5	2.45	1.62	− 0.83

The concentration of sucrose in solution ≡ zero mass change = 1.1%.
Therefore, the concentration of sucrose in potato tuber tissue = 1.1%.

Notes

1. Osmosis is the movement of water particles through a semipermeable membrane from high concentration of water to low concentration until equilibrium is established.

2. Cell membranes are semipermeable. If the concentration of sucrose in cells is greater than the concentration of sucrose in the solution bathing them, water particles will move into the cells faster than water particles leave the cells and the potato cylinders will gain mass and expand until equilibrium is established and vice versa.

3. If the concentration of sucrose in the cells and the solution bathing them is the same then the system will already be in equilibrium and there will be no change in mass of the potato cylinders.

4. The activity can be extended at A-level by asking students to carry out statistical analysis on the data and apply the appropriate test for levels of significance.

2.8 Diffusion of solids in agar gel

A rack of four boiling tubes containing agar gel and closed with bungs
Iodine
Potassium manganate(VII)

Potassium dichromate(VI)
Copper(II) sulfate(VI)
Spatula
Eye protection

Safety Agar powder is harmful if inhaled so take the appropriate precautions when handling this material. Potassium manganate(VII) and potassium dichromate(VI) are both powerful oxidising agents. Potassium dichromate(VI) is toxic and may cause skin sensitisation. It is a category 2 carcinogen and only the teacher should handle it. Protective gloves should be worn. Solid copper(II) sulfate(VI) is harmful. Iodine is harmful by skin contact. Ensure that any spilled solids are disposed of safely.

Method

1. Remove the bungs from the boiling tubes and put a level spatula measure of each of the four solids on top of the agar gel in each boiling tube.

2. Replace the bungs and study the appearance of the gels after one week.

Sample results

The gels became impregnated with the colour of the substances which had been applied to the surface.

Notes

1. The results show diffusion between the gel and the solid which had been applied to its surface.

2. Prepare the gel from a hot 10% solution of agar in distilled water.

2.9 How big are particles?

Pneumatic trough
Measuring cylinder ($10\,cm^3$)
Pepper pot containing flowers of
    sulfur or lycopodium powder

Teat pipette (dropper)
Ruler
$0.1\,cm^3$ of castor oil in $100\,cm^3$ of
    petroleum ether (60–80 °C)

Safety Petroleum ether is harmful and highly flammable. It is also a solvent which will dissolve the natural oils of the skin, so avoid skin contact. Avoid all naked flames.

Method

1. Fill the trough with tap water.

2. Sprinkle a fine layer of powder from the pepper pot onto the surface of the water.

3. Add one drop of oil from the dropper to the centre of the layer of powder on the surface of the water.

4. Measure the diameter of the 'circle' which is produced.

5. Measure the volume of 100 drops of oil from the same dropper and find the volume for one drop.

6. Calculate the height (h) of the oil film from:

$$\text{volume} = \pi \times d^2 \div 4 \times h$$

Sample results

1. Diameter $= 13\,cm$

2. Volume of 100 drops of oil-petroleum ether mixture $= 4.8\,cm^3$

Calculations

1. Volume of one drop of oil-petroleum ether mixture = $0.048 \, cm^3$

2. Volume of oil in one drop of the mixture

   = $0.048 \div 1000 = 4.8 \times 10^{-5} \, cm^3$

   Rearranging the equation above:

   $h = 4.8 \times 10^{-5} \times 4 \div (\pi \times 13 \times 13)$

   = $3.6 \times 10^{-7} \, cm$

Note

The experiment relies on the petroleum ether evaporating quickly and the oil spreading out in a layer one particle thick so that the height of the oil film is the diameter of an oil particle.

2.10 Observing the growth of crystals

Hot saturated solutions of: potassium nitrate(V), ammonium chloride, ammonium nitrate(V), and aluminium potassium sulfate(VI)

Four teat pipettes (droppers)
Microscope and slides
Eye protection

Safety Potassium nitrate(V) and ammonium nitrate(V) are oxidising agents and can cause fire with combustible materials.

Method

1. Focus the microscope with the ×10 lens in place using a hair.

2. Place one drop of hot saturated solution onto the microscope slide which should already be in the correct position and in focus. Observe the crystals forming as the solution cools.

3. Repeat with each of the hot saturated solutions.

Sample results

All crystals of the same substance had the same shape.

potassium nitrate(V)	needles
ammonium nitrate(V)	needles
ammonium chloride	snow-flakes
aluminium potassium sulfate(VI)	cubes

Note

The results are evidence for the orderly arrangement of particles in crystals.

2.11 How many particles make up one mole?

Agar salt bridge (see Note 1 below)
Four connecting leads with 4 mm plugs at each end
Two graphite rods mounted in separate rubber bungs
Two retort stands with clamps
Two crocodile clips
12 V dc supply
Two beakers (100 cm³)
Ammeter (0–10 mA)

Rheostat
Potassium chloride solution ($0.2 \, mol \, dm^{-3}$)
Hydrochloric acid ($0.001 \, mol \, dm^{-3}$)
Phenolphthalein indicator solution
Teat pipette (dropper)
Pipette (25 cm³)
Pipette filler
Stop-watch

Safety Inhaling agar powder is hazardous to health so observe safety precautions in preparing the salt bridge.

Method

1. Set up the apparatus as shown in Figure 2.4.

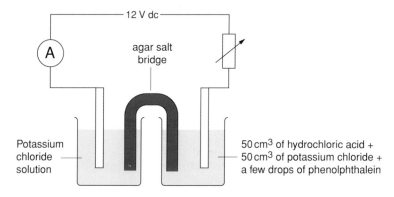

Figure 2.4 Determination of the Avogadro constant.

2. Switch on the current and start the stop-watch.

3. Using the rheostat, adjust the current to between 8–10 mA.

4. Gently swirl the beaker which contains the negative electrode and measure the time for the solution in the beaker to turn pink.

5. Using the current and the time you can calculate the charge flowing.

You know how many moles of acid required this charge to decompose so you can find the charge needed for one mole. Using the charge on the electron you can calculate the number of electrons in 1 mole.

Sample results

1. Time for solution to turn pink = 600 seconds
2. Current flowing = 8 mA

Calculations

Charge = current $\times$ time = $0.008 \times 600 = 4.8$ coulomb

Concentration of acid = 0.001 mol dm^{-3}
so 50 cm^3 contains $50 \div 1000 \times 0.001 = 5 \times 10^{-5}$ mol

5×10^{-5} mol required 4.8 coulomb
so 1 mol required $4.8 \div (5 \times 10^{-5})$ coulomb $= 9.6 \times 10^4$ coulomb

The charge on the electron = 1.6×10^{-19} coulomb
So number of electrons in 1 mol = $9.6 \times 10^4 \div (1.6 \times 10^{-19})$
$= 6 \times 10^{23}$ = Avogadro constant.

Notes

1. Prepare the agar salt bridge by heating together 300 cm^3 of saturated potassium chloride solution, 50 cm^3 distilled water and 10 g of powdered agar. Pour the warm mixture into a glass U-tube and leave to gel.
2. The equations for the reactions that occur at the cathode in this experiment are:

    When acid: $H_3O^+ \rightarrow H^+ + H_2O$

    When acid is spent: $H_2O \rightarrow H^+ + OH^-$

    $2H^+ + 2e^- \rightarrow H_2$

3. The end point is reached when the negatively charged OH^- ions predominate and change the colour of the indicator to pink.

2.12 Effect of molar mass on the effusion of gases

Measuring cylinder (1 dm³)
Stop-watch
Apparatus to produce: hydrogen, carbon dioxide, oxygen and argon (see Chapter 16)
Two retort stands with clamps
Ice-cream tub
Burette (50 cm³)
Eye protection

Effusion tube: This consists of 5 cm of glass tubing with a rubber sleeve at one end to fit over the nozzle of the burette, and a disc of aluminium cooking foil cemented with epoxy resin over the other end of the glass tubing. Use a needle to make the finest hole possible in the aluminium foil disc

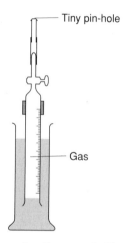

Figure 2.5 Measuring the rate of effusion of gases.

Safety Low hazard.

Method

1. Fill the ice-cream tub with tap water.

2. Close the burette tap and fill the burette with tap water, cover the top with your finger, invert the burette and place the covered end under the water and secure it in position with the retort stand and clamp. Remove your finger and the water should remain in the burette.

3. Displace the water in the inverted burette with gas.

4. Close the inverted burette with your finger and transfer the burette

to a measuring cylinder filled with water. Remove your finger and secure the burette in position with a retort stand and clamp.

5. Fit the effusion tube over the nozzle of the burette (see Figure 2.5).

6. Adjust the water level in the burette using the burette tap.

7. Simultaneously, open the burette tap and start the stop-watch to measure the time for the water to push $20\,cm^3$ of gas out of the burette.

8. Repeat the procedure for the different gases.

9. Plot a line graph of molar mass on the x-axis and $(time/s)^2$ on the y-axis.

Sample results

Gas	Molar mass	Time for 20 cm³ to effuse/s
Hydrogen	2	4
Argon	40	17
Carbon dioxide	44	19
Oxygen	32	16
Air	29	15

Notes

1. Effusion is the passage of gas through a small orifice or porous material from a region of higher pressure to a region of lower pressure. Graham's law of diffusion will apply.

2. From Graham's law: Rate of effusion is inversely proportional to the square root of density. Density = mass/volume, so rate is proportional to the square root of volume/mass.

   By Avogadro's hypothesis, equal volumes of all gases contain the same number of particles. If the volume of the gases is constant, density is proportional to mass which is also proportional to molar mass. This means that Graham's law can be written: Rate is inversely proportional to the square root of molar mass.

   Rate of effusion = volume ÷ time. Since volume was the same for all gases, 1÷ time is proportional to the square root of 1 ÷ molar mass or, the time squared for equal volumes of all gases to effuse, is directly proportional to the molar mass. Therefore a graph of the time squared for a constant volume of different gases to effuse against the molar mass of the gases should be linear and intercept the origin.

3. The size of the aperture in the effusion tube will affect the rate of effusion so it is important to use the same effusion tube with all of the gases.

4. Avoid getting any water onto the aluminium foil of the effusion tube, otherwise it may obstruct the aperture.

3 SOLUBILITY

When a solid dissolves in a liquid, the particles of the solid occupy the spaces between the particles of the liquid and so become evenly dispersed thoughout. The resulting mixture is called a solution. The liquid that dissolves the solid is called the solvent. The substance which dissolves in the solvent is called the solute. A solution is a homogeneous mixture of solute and solvent. When all of the spaces between the solvent particles are occupied by solute particles, the solution is saturated and no more solute will dissolve at that particular temperature. If the temperature of the solvent is raised, then the spaces between the particles become bigger, so more solute particles can be accommodated in the solution. Conversely, if the temperature of the solution is lowered, then the spaces between the particles of the solvent gets smaller, so fewer solute particles can be accommodated and solute will precipitate until a new state of saturation occurs. Solubility is the mass of solute which will saturate 100 g of solvent at a given temperature.

3.1 Investigating the solubility of a variety of salts in water

Distilled water

Test-tubes

Carbonates, chlorides, sulfate(VI)s
  and nitrate(V)s of ammonium,
  sodium, potassium, calcium,
  magnesium, lead and copper

Spatula

Bunsen burner

Measuring cylinder (10 cm^3)

Eye protection

Safety Lead salts are toxic. The effects are cumulative. Pregnant women or younger pupils should not handle these substances. There is the danger of damage to the unborn child. Wash hands after using solutions. Copper compounds are harmful if swallowed. Solutions containing copper are skin irritants. Nitrate(V)s are oxidising agents and cause fire with combustible materials. Calcium chloride is irritant.

Method

1. Using a spatula, take a small sample, enough to cover a finger nail, of each substance and add it to 5 cm^3 of distilled water in test-tubes.

2. Warm the mixture over a Bunsen flame. Use gentle heating and shake the test-tube to prevent bumping. Note whether or not the

substance dissolves. If the substance dissolves, it will 'disappear' and the solution will become clear.

Sample results

Cation	Anion			
	Carbonate	Chloride	Sulfate(VI)	Nitrate(V)
Sodium	soluble	soluble	soluble	soluble
Potassium	soluble	soluble	soluble	soluble
Magnesium	insoluble	soluble	soluble	soluble
Calcium	insoluble	soluble	partially soluble	soluble
Lead(II)	insoluble	insoluble	insoluble	soluble
Copper(II)	insoluble	soluble	soluble	soluble
Ammonium	soluble	soluble	soluble	soluble

Notes

1. All ammonium salts and salts of alkali metals are soluble.
2. All nitrate(V)s are soluble.
3. All carbonates are insoluble except those of ammonium and alkali metals.
4. All chlorides are soluble except lead(II) chloride and silver chloride.
5. All sulfate(VI)s are soluble except lead(II) sulfate(VI) and barium sulfate(VI).
6. The only soluble salts of lead are lead(II) nitrate(V) and lead(II) ethanoate.

3.2 Testing the solubility of a variety of substances in various solvents

Test-tubes with corks
Distilled water
Cyclohexane
Ethanol
Sodium chloride
Sucrose

Paraffin wax scrapings
Sand
Measuring cylinder (10 cm^3)
Spatula
Eye protection

Safety Cyclohexane and ethanol are both highly flammable. Cyclohexane is harmful and dissolves natural oils from the skin so avoid skin contact.

Method

1. Repeat the procedure described in 3.1 using distilled water, cyclohexane and ethanol as solvents. Do not heat the mixtures because cyclohexane and ethanol vapours are highly flammable.

2. Cork the tubes and shake them to see if the solutes dissolve.

Sample results

Solute	Solvent		
	Water	Ethanol	Cyclohexane
Sodium chloride	soluble	insoluble	insoluble
Wax	insoluble	insoluble	soluble
Sand	insoluble	insoluble	insoluble
Sucrose	soluble	soluble	insoluble

Notes

1. Substances able to form intermolecular bonds with solvent particles will dissolve.

2. Water and ethanol are hydrogen-bonded liquids. Sucrose molecules contain OH groups which can participate in hydrogen bonding so sucrose is soluble in these solvents.

3. Wax and cyclohexane are both van der Waals bonded so wax is soluble in cyclohexane but not in hydrogen-bonded solvents.

4. Sand is a macromolecular covalently bonded lattice of silicon dioxide (silicon(IV) oxide) and as such is insoluble in all three solvents. It will dissolve in liquid HF.

5. Sodium chloride is ionic and the ions hydrate in aqueous solution.

3.3 The ammonia fountain experiment

Ammonia production apparatus (see Chapter 16)
Distilled water
Retort stand and clamp
Pneumatic trough
Litmus solution (100 cm^3)
Round-bottomed flask (500 cm^3)
Two-holed rubber bung for the flask

Teat pipette
Glass tubing (10 cm)
Rubber tubing
Two rubber-tubing clamps
Red litmus paper
Sulfuric(VI) acid (1 mol dm^{-3})
Eye protection

Safety Ammonia is toxic by inhalation and can cause asthma attacks in susceptible people so make sure the room is well ventilated beforehand. The production of ammonia and filling the flask should be carried out in a fume cupboard. Eye protection is essential. Check that the flask is sound and free from cracks. 1 mol dm^{-3} sulfuric(VI) acid is irritant.

Method

1. In a fume cupboard, fill a round-bottomed flask with ammonia using the apparatus in Figure 16.2, Chapter 16.

2. Using the round-bottomed flask shown in Figure 3.1, connect tube A to the ammonia production apparatus and fill the flask with ammonia.

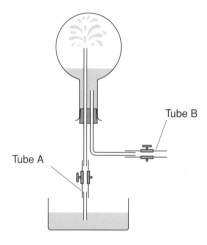

Figure 3.1 The ammonia fountain.

3. Check that the flask is full by holding damp red litmus paper under tube B. When ammonia escapes from tube B the red litmus paper turns blue and the flask will be full of ammonia.

4. Clamp both tubes A and B and disconnect tube A from the ammonia production apparatus.

5. Fill the pneumatic trough with water and add the litmus solution.

6. Add a drop of sulfuric(VI) acid to acidify the water. The litmus turns red.

7. Support the flask with the clamp and stand so that tube A is immersed in the pneumatic trough of water containing red litmus.

8. Introduce a little distilled water into tube B. Pinch the tube between the finger and thumb, release the clamp and 'milk' the distilled water into the flask, then replace the clamp. Only a drop of water is required to enter the flask at this stage of the procedure.

9. Tube A should remain immersed in the pneumatic trough containing acidified water and red litmus. Release the clamp on tube A.

Sample results

After a short delay, a fountain of blue liquid emerges from the teat pipette nozzle inside the flask.

Notes

1. The fountain is caused by the ammonia inside the flask dissolving in the drop of distilled water introduced through tube B. This decreases the pressure inside the flask and atmospheric pressure forces the water in the pneumatic trough into the flask via the teat pipette. As more water enters the flask, more ammonia dissolves to maintain a decrease in pressure. When all of the ammonia has dissolved, the fountain stops.

2. Ammonia is alkaline and so the colour of the red litmus changes to blue.

3.4 Determination of the solubility of potassium nitrate(V) in water at room temperature

Boiling tube	Spoon spatula
Boiling tube holder	Evaporating basin
Distilled water	Bunsen burner
Potassium nitrate(V)	Tripod and gauze
Thermometer	Top-pan balance
Measuring cylinder ($10\,cm^3$)	Eye protection

Safety Potassium nitrate(V) is an oxidising agent and can cause fire with combustible materials. Ensure that the students know how to heat a boiling tube of liquid safely. Eye protection is essential.

Method

1. Put $20\,cm^3$ of distilled water into the boiling tube and heat it using the Bunsen burner.

2. Add $10\,g$ of potassium nitrate(V) to the hot water in the boiling tube and continue heating until it has dissolved.

3. Stop heating, immerse a thermometer in the solution and cool the tube under a cold running tap until the temperature is 20 °C. Potassium nitrate(V) crystals will precipitate and the supernatant liquor will be saturated.

4. Weigh the evaporating basin.

5. Decant 10 cm^3 of the supernatant into the measuring cylinder and then transfer it to the previously weighed evaporating basin.

6. Weigh the evaporating basin and supernatant and find the mass of the supernatant by subtraction.

7. Evaporate the supernatant to dryness. Beware! May start spitting as it approaches dryness. Reweigh the basin and residue. Find the mass of the residue by subtraction.

8. Find the mass of water in the supernatant by subtracting the mass of the residue from the mass of the supernatant.

9. Calculate the mass of residue which would have dissolved in 100 g of distilled water. This gives the solubility of potassium nitrate(V) at 20 °C.

Sample results

1. Mass of basin = 15.18 g
2. Mass of basin + supernatant = 27.13 g
3. Mass of supernatant = 11.95 g
4. Mass of basin + residue = 18.04 g
5. Mass of residue = 2.86 g
6. Mass of water in supernatant = 9.09 g

Calculations

9.09 g of water dissolved 2.86 g of KNO$_3$

1 g of water dissolved 2.86 ÷ 9.09 g of KNO$_3$

100 g of water dissolved (2.86 ÷ 9.09) × 100 g of KNO$_3$

Therefore the solubility of KNO$_3$ at 20 °C = 31.5 g/100 g

3.5 Investigating the effect of temperature on the solubility of potassium nitrate(V)

Boiling tube
Boiling-tube holder
Measuring cylinder ($10\,cm^3$)
Distilled water
Spatula
Top-pan balance

Potassium nitrate(V)
Thermometer
Scrap paper
Bunsen burner
Eye protection

Safety As for 3.4.

Method

1. Weigh out one 4 g sample and four 1 g samples of potassium nitrate(V) onto scrap paper.

2. Put $10\,cm^3$ of distilled water into the boiling tube and add the 4 g sample of potassium nitrate(V).

3. Heat the mixture until all of the potassium nitrate(V) has dissolved.

4. Stop heating and immerse a thermometer in the solution.

5. Cool the solution under a cold running tap and measure the temperature when crystals first begin to appear. This gives the temperature at which the solubility of potassium nitrate(V) = $40\,g/100\,g$

6. Add the other samples of potassium nitrate(V), 1 g at a time, and repeat the procedure until all of the potassium nitrate(V) has been added.

7. Draw a line graph of temperature/°C on the x-axis and solubility of potassium nitrate(V)/g per 100 g on the y-axis.

Sample results

Solubility KNO_3 / g per 100 g	Temperature/°C
40	25
50	32
60	38
70	43
80	47

4 FORMULAE, EQUATIONS and QUANTITATIVE CHEMISTRY

A chemical formula is a combination of chemical symbols which shows the number of atoms of each element in the structure of one molecule or ion. The empirical formula shows only the elements present and the ratio between their number of atoms. The molecular formula shows the total number of the atoms of each element present. The structural formula shows the order and arrangement of the atoms present, e.g. for ethane:

Empirical formula = CH_3

Molecular formula = C_2H_6

$$\text{Structural formula} = \begin{array}{c} \quad\ \ \text{H} \quad\ \text{H} \\ \quad\ \ | \qquad | \\ \text{H}-\text{C}-\text{C}-\text{H} \\ \quad\ \ | \qquad | \\ \quad\ \ \text{H} \quad\ \text{H} \end{array}$$

A chemical equation is a way of representing a chemical reaction using symbols for the participating particles. A single arrow is used to represent a reaction going in one direction only and a double half arrow for a reversible reaction(see Chapter 14). The reactants are shown on the left of the arrow and the products on the right. When reactions involve different phases it is usual to put the phase symbol in brackets after the chemical symbol to which it refers. There should be the same number of atoms at the end of the reaction as there were at the beginning and so equations should show the relative numbers of particles reacting. This is denoted using whole numbers which immediately precede the chemical formula of the reacting particle. These numbers are the stoichiometric coefficients.

For example, for the reaction between magnesium and hydrochloric acid:

$$Mg(s) + 2HCl(aq) \rightarrow MgCl_2(aq) + H_2(g)$$

The amount of substance in a certain volume of solution is called its concentration. Concentration is expressed as mass per unit volume, e.g. g dm^{-3}, or mol dm^{-3}. One mole is the mass of substance which contains the Avogadro number of particles and is the relative formula mass expressed in grams. The relative formula mass is the sum of the relative masses in grams of all of the atoms which make up one molecule of the substance, e.g. a molecule of oxygen is O_2. The relative atomic mass of oxygen is 16. So one mole of oxygen = 32 g.

4.1 Conservation of mass in chemical reactions

Potassium iodide solution
($1\,mol\,dm^{-3}$)
Lead(II) nitrate(V) solution ($1\,mol\,dm^{-3}$)
Conical flask ($250\,cm^3$) fitted with a
bung
Test tube ($100 \times 16\,mm$)
Measuring cylinder ($25\,cm^3$)

Top-pan balance
Suction pump
Buchner funnel and flask
Filter paper
Distilled water
Forceps
Eye protection

Safety Lead salts are toxic. The effects are cumulative. Pregnant women or younger pupils should not handle these substances. There is the danger of damage to the unborn child. Wash hands after using solution.

Method

1. Using the measuring cylinder, transfer $25\,cm^3$ of potassium iodide solution to the conical flask.

2. Put $10\,cm^3$ of lead(II) nitrate(V) solution into the test-tube.

3. Put the test-tube into the conical flask and prop it upright so that the two solutions do not mix.

4. Close the flask with the bung and weigh the flask with its contents.

5. Mix the contents of the flask and then reweigh.

6. Quantitatively filter off the precipitate through a previously weighed filter paper using the Buchner funnel and flask connected to the suction pump. Wash the precipitate with distilled water.

7. Remove the filter paper and precipitate from the Buchner funnel using forceps and place them in an oven set at $100\,^\circ C$ to dry.

8. Weigh the dry filter paper and precipitate.

9. Find the mass of the precipitate by subtracting the mass of the filter paper from the mass of the filter paper + precipitate.

Sample results

A yellow precipitate of lead iodide formed.

Mass of the flask + contents before mixing = 227.6 g

Mass of the flask + contents after mixing = 227.6 g

Mass of filter paper = 0.9 g

Mass of filter paper + precipitate = 5.5 g

Mass of precipitate = 4.6 g

Notes

1. The formation of the precipitate showed that a chemical reaction had taken place.

2. The bung prevented any material entering or leaving the flask.

3. The mass, before and after the reaction, remained the same.

4. Atoms are not created nor destroyed during chemical reactions. They are simply rearranged in forming new molecules. This is why chemical equations must balance, i.e. the number of each sort of atom on both sides of the equation must be the same.

5. The mass of precipitate formed is consistent with the calculated value according to the equation:

$$Pb(NO_3)_2(aq) + 2KI(aq) \rightarrow PbI_2(s) + 2KNO_3(aq)$$

4.2 Determination of the formula for copper(II) oxide by reduction with methane

Bunsen burner
Clamp and stand
Copper(II) oxide
Methane supply
Spatula
Eye protection

Test-tube with a small hole in the bottom and fitted with a bung and rubber tubing
Porcelain boat
Forceps
Top-pan balance

Safety Copper compounds are harmful. Safety screens must be used. Eye protection is essential.

Method

1. Weigh the porcelain boat empty and again containing copper oxide.

2. Find the mass of copper(II) oxide in the boat by subtracting the mass of the boat from the mass of the boat + copper(II) oxide.

3. Assemble the apparatus as shown in Figure 4.1.

4. Using forceps, place the boat inside the test-tube, fit the bung and connect the rubber tubing to the gas supply.

5. Light the Bunsen burner. Slowly turn the gas tap to which the rubber tubing from the test-tube has been connected. Allow the gas to flow

for a few seconds to flush out the air. Then hold the Bunsen burner flame near the hole in the end of the test-tube. The gas escaping from the hole will ignite. Regulate the gas supply to produce a 5 cm flame.

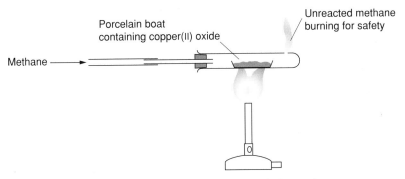

Figure 4.1 Reduction of copper(II) oxide by methane.

6. Heat the test-tube under the boat until all of the copper(II) oxide in the boat turns brown. When this happens, the copper(II) oxide has been reduced to copper.

7. Remove the Bunsen burner but keep the flame from the hole of the test-tube burning until the test-tube is cool enough to touch.

8. Extinguish the flame by turning off the gas supply, disconnect the apparatus and remove the boat using forceps.

9. Reweigh the boat.

10. Reassemble the apparatus and repeat the process until the mass of the boat plus copper is constant.

11. Find the mass of copper by subtracting the mass of the boat from the mass of the boat + copper.

12. Find the mass of oxygen in the original copper(II) oxide by subtracting the mass of copper from the mass of copper(II) oxide.

13. Convert to moles by dividing the masses of copper and oxygen by their respective relative atomic masses and then to a whole number ratio. This gives the formula of the original copper(II) oxide.

Sample results

Mass of boat = 12.73 g

Mass of boat + copper(II) oxide = 14.32 g

Mass of copper(II) oxide = 1.59 g

Mass of boat + copper = 14.00 g

Mass of copper = 1.27 g

Mass of oxygen = 0.32 g

Calculations

Moles of copper = 1.27 ÷ 64 = 0.02

Moles of oxygen = 0.32 ÷ 16 = 0.02

Ratio between moles of copper to moles of oxygen = 1:1

Formula for copper(II) oxide = Cu_1O_1 or CuO

Notes

1. The equation for the reaction is:

   $$4CuO(s) + CH_4(g) \rightarrow 4Cu(s) + 2H_2O(l) + CO_2(g)$$

2. It is important to keep the flame from the hole in the test-tube burning until the reduced copper(II) oxide is cool, otherwise oxidation of the hot copper will occur by air entering through the hole in the test-tube as the gas inside contracts.

3. The experiment will still work if the gas supply is propane.

4. To put a hole in the bottom of a test-tube, close the tube with a rubber bung and heat the bottom of the tube just above the blue cone of a roaring Bunsen burner flame. The increased pressure of the hot air inside the tube will blow the hole when the bottom of the tube melts.

4.3 Determination of the formula for magnesium oxide by heating magnesium in air

Porcelain crucible with lid
Tongs
Magnesium ribbon
Scissors
Bunsen burner

Tripod
Pipe-clay triangle
Top-pan balance
Eye protection

Safety Magnesium is highly flammable. Eye protection is essential. Closely supervise the distribution of magnesium ribbon to prevent theft.

Method

1. Weigh the crucible with its lid.
2. Cut 20 cm of magnesium ribbon into small pieces and collect the pieces in the crucible.
3. Weigh the crucible + lid + magnesium and find the mass of magnesium by subtracting the mass of the crucible and lid from the mass of the crucible + lid + magnesium.
4. Put the crucible on the pipe-clay triangle on the tripod. Heat to constant weight with the Bunsen burner whilst tilting the lid with tongs to expose the burning magnesium to the air to form magnesium oxide.
5. When cool, weigh the crucible + lid + magnesium oxide.
6. Find the mass of magnesium oxide by subtraction.
7. Find the mass of oxygen which reacted with the magnesium by subtraction.
8. Convert the masses of magnesium and oxygen to moles by dividing by their respective relative atomic masses. The whole number ratio gives the formula for magnesium oxide.

Sample results

Mass of crucible + lid = 28.32 g

Mass of crucible + lid + magnesium = 28.56 g

Mass of magnesium = 0.24 g

Mass of crucible + lid + magnesium oxide = 28.72 g

Mass of magnesium oxide = 0.40 g

Mass of oxygen = 0.16 g

Calculations

Moles of magnesium = $0.24 \div 24 = 0.01$

Moles of oxygen = $0.16 \div 16 = 0.01$

Ratio between moles of magnesium and moles of oxygen = 1:1

Formula = Mg_1O_1 or MgO

Note

Equation for the reaction:

$$2Mg(s) + O_2(g) \rightarrow 2MgO(s)$$

4.4 Finding the stoichiometry of the reaction between acid and alkali using a pH indicator

Conical flask (100 cm³)
Teat pipette (dropper)
Hydrochloric acid (0.1 mol dm⁻³)
Sulfuric(VI) acid (0.1 mol dm⁻³)
Sodium hydroxide solution (0.1 mol dm⁻³)

Phenolphthalein indicator solution
Distilled water
Eye protection

Safety The alkali is an irritant. Be extra vigilant with alkali in droppers. Eye protection is essential. Phenolphthalein is a purgative and is dissolved in a highly flammable solvent.

Method

1. Using the dropper, add 20 drops of sodium hydroxide solution to the conical flask and dilute with a little water.

2. Add 3 drops of indicator and swirl the flask to mix.

3. Add sulfuric(VI) acid dropwise, swirling the flask to mix after the addition of each drop and count the number of drops required to decolorise the indicator.

4. Repeat the procedure using hydrochloric acid instead of sulfuric(VI) acid.

Sample results

10 drops of H_2SO_4 neutralised 20 drops of NaOH and 20 drops of HCl neutralised 20 drops of NaOH.

Note

Because all reagents were equimolar, the ratio between the number of drops gives the stoichiometry of the respective equations so:

$H_2SO_4(aq) + 2NaOH(aq) \rightarrow Na_2SO_4(aq) + H_2O(l)$

$HCl + NaOH \rightarrow NaCl + H_2O$

4.5 Following the course of the reaction between copper(II) sulfate(VI) and sodium hydroxide by measuring temperature

Copper(II) sulfate(VI) solution
($1\,mol\,dm^{-3}$)
Sodium hydroxide solution
($1\,mol\,dm^{-3}$)
Expanded polystyrene drinks cup

Thermometer
Measuring cylinder ($50\,cm^3$)
Burette ($50\,cm^3$)
Clamp and stand
Eye protection

Safety Copper(II) sulfate(VI) solution is harmful and a skin irritant. Sodium hydroxide solution is corrosive at this concentration and goggles (not safety specs) should be worn.

Method

1. Using the measuring cylinder, transfer $50\,cm^3$ of sodium hydroxide solution to the cup.

2. Fill the burette with copper(II) sulfate(VI) solution and hold it with the clamp.

3. Add the copper(II) sulfate(VI) solution from the burette, $5\,cm^3$ at a time and until $50\,cm^3$ has been added.

4. Stir with the thermometer and record the temperature after each $5\,cm^3$ addition. It is important to add the next $5\,cm^3$ as soon as the maximum temperature caused by the previous $5\,cm^3$ addition is reached.

5. Plot a line graph of volume of copper(II) sulfate(VI) solution added/ cm^3, on the x-axis and temperature/ $°C$ on the y-axis. The maximum temperature occurs at the end point of the reaction.

Sample results

$CuSO_4/cm^3$	Temp/$°C$	$CuSO_4/cm^3$	Temp/$°C$
0	22	30	28
5	24	35	28
10	25	40	27
15	26	45	27
20	27	50	26
25	28		

Notes

1. The maximum temperature occurred after the addition of 25 cm³ of copper(II) sulfate(VI) solution.

2. Because the reagents were equimolar, the ratio between the volumes of the reagents gives the stoichiometry of the reaction.

3. 25 cm³ of copper(II) sulfate(VI) reacted with 50 cm³ of sodium hydroxide so the equation is:

$$CuSO_4 + 2NaOH \rightarrow Cu(OH)_2 + Na_2SO_4$$

4. An indicator cannot be used for this reaction because one of the reagents is already coloured and this will mask the colour of the indicator.

4.6 Following the course of the reaction between lead(IV) nitrate(V) and potassium iodide by measuring the height of the precipitate

Lead(IV) nitrate(V) solution (1 mol dm⁻³) (dispense using a burette)
Potassium iodide solution (1 mol dm⁻³)
Ruler

Five test-tubes
Test-tube rack
Measuring cylinder (10 cm³)
Hand lens
Eye protection

Safety Lead(IV) nitrate(V) solution is toxic. The effects are cumulative. Pregnant women or younger pupils should not handle this substance. There is the danger of damage to the unborn child. Wash hands after using solution.

Method

1. Using the measuring cylinder, transfer 5 cm³ of potassium iodide solution into each tube.

2. Add the lead(IV) nitrate(V) solution in successive 1.0 cm³ increments to the 5 cm³ of potassium iodide in each tube and mix.

3. When the precipitate has settled measure the height of the precipitate using the ruler and hand lens.

4. Plot a line graph of volume of lead(IV) nitrate(V) added/ cm³ on the x-axis and height of the precipitate/mm on the y-axis and interpolate the minimum volume of lead(IV)) nitrate(V) which gave

the maximum height of precipitate. This indicates the stoichiometric mixture.

Sample results

Lead(IV) nitrate(V)/ cm^3	Height of precipitate/ mm
1	5
2	8
3	13
4	12
5	14

Note

Maximum height of the precipitate occurred when 2.5 cm^3 of lead(IV) nitrate(V) had been added. Since the reagents were equimolar the stoichiometry of the reaction is 1:2, so the equation is:

$$Pb(NO_3)_2(aq) + 2KI(aq) \rightarrow PbI_2(s) + 2KNO_3(aq)$$

4.7 Determination of relative atomic mass of lithium by measuring volume of hydrogen produced when the metal reacts with water

Apparatus shown in Figure 16.1, but no thistle funnel
Lithium
Scalpel
Forceps
White ceramic tile
Absorbent tissue

Conical flask fitted with a bung and delivery tube
Ice-cream tub
Clamp and stand
Measuring cylinder (250 cm^3)
Distilled water
Top-pan balance
Eye protection

Safety Handle lithium using forceps because it will react with moisture from the skin. Hydrogen–air mixtures are explosive. The lithium hydroxide solution formed by the reaction is corrosive so avoid contact with skin and eyes. Eye protection is essential.

Method

1. Set up the apparatus as shown in Experiment 16.1.

2. Put 50 cm^3 of distilled water into the conical flask.

3. Blot a piece of lithium with an absorbent tissue and place it, using forceps, on a ceramic tile. Cut off about 0.1 g of the metal and weigh it.

4. Put the piece of lithium in the conical flask containing the water and quickly fit the bung.

5. Measure the volume of gas produced after the reaction has finished.

6. Calculate the relative atomic mass of lithium given that 1 mole of gas occupies $24\,dm^3$ at room temperature and pressure.

Sample results

Mass of lithium taken = 0.12 g

Volume of gas produced = $200\,cm^3$

Calculations

$200\,cm^3$ of gas = 8.3×10^{-3} mol

From equation:

$$2Li + 2H_2O \rightarrow 2LiOH + H_2$$

1 mole of hydrogen is produced by 2 moles of Li, so 8.3×10^{-3} moles is produced by 16.6×10^{-3} moles of Li. The mass of lithium taken was 0.12 g.

If 16.6×10^{-3} mol = 0.12 g, then 1 mol = $0.12 \div (16.6 \times 10^{-3}) = 7.2$ g.

Therefore the relative atomic mass of lithium = 7.2.

Notes

1. The published value for the relative atomic mass of lithium is 7.

2. The same experiment can be carried out to find the volume occupied by 1 mole of gas at room temperature by knowing the relative atomic mass of lithium and carrying out the appropriate calculations.

4.8 Coulometric titration between barium hydroxide and sulfuric(VI) acid

Sulfuric(VI) acid ($0.1\,mol\,dm^{-3}$)

Barium hydroxide solution ($0.1\,mol\,dm^{-3}$)

Beaker ($100\,cm^3$)

Two graphite rods 1 cm apart and mounted in a bung

Two crocodile clips

Ammeter (0–1 A)

Three connecting leads with 4 mm plugs at each end.

Burette ($50\,cm^3$)

6 V dc power supply

Pipette ($25\,cm^3$)

Pipette filler

Clamp and stand

Eye protection

Safety Barium compounds are harmful at this concentration.

Method

1. Set up the apparatus as shown in Figure 4.2.
2. Measure 25 cm^3 barium hydroxide into the beaker. Add the sulfuric(VI) acid 5 cm^3 at a time until 50 cm^3 have been added. After each addition swirl the beaker to mix and measure the current flowing.
3. Plot a line graph of volume of sulfuric(VI) acid added/cm^3, on the x-axis and current flowing/A, on the y-axis. The mixture has the lowest conductivity at the end point.

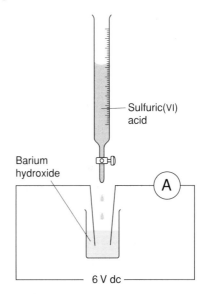

Figure 4.2 Coulometric titration.

Sample results

H$_2$SO$_4$/cm^3	Current/A	H$_2$SO$_4$/cm^3	Current/A
0	0.15	30	0.10
5	0.13	35	0.16
10	0.10	40	0.21
15	0.08	45	0.27
20	0.05	50	0.32
25	0.02		

Notes

1. The lowest conductivity occurred when the mixture contained 25 cm^3 of both reagents. The reagents were equimolar so the stoichiometry

for the reaction was 1:1. The equation for the reaction therefore is:

$$Ba(OH)_2 + H_2SO_4 \rightarrow BaSO_4 + 2H_2O$$

2. The current flowing decreased as the end point was approached because barium ions were being precipitated and undissociated water was being formed. The current increased after the end point because of the build-up of ions from the addition of sulfuric(VI) acid.

4.9 Determination of the concentration of an acid by acid-base titration using a pH indicator

Pipette ($25\,cm^3$)
Pipette filler
Burette ($50\,cm^3$)
Retort stand and clamp
White ceramic tile
pH indicator (see Note 1)

Conical flask ($250\,cm^3$)
Sulfuric(VI) acid ($0.1\,mol\,dm^{-3}$)
Sodium hydroxide solution
  (approx. $0.1\,mol\,dm^{-3}$)
Eye protection

Safety The alkali is irritant at this concentration.

Method

1. Fill the burette with sulfuric(VI) acid and hold the burette in a clamp and stand.

2. Using a safety filler, pipette $25\,cm^3$ of sodium hydroxide solution into the conical flask and place it on a white ceramic tile.

3. Add 3–5 drops of indicator and run in the acid from the burette until one drop changes the colour of the indicator. The conical flask should be swirled whilst the acid is run in.

4. Record the burette reading and repeat the procedure until two burette readings which agree within $0.1\,cm^3$ are obtained.

Sample results

$12.3\,cm^3$ of H_2SO_4 neutralised $25\,cm^3$ of NaOH.

Calculations

From equation:

$$H_2SO_4 + 2NaOH \rightarrow Na_2SO_4 + 2H_2O$$

2 moles of NaOH react with 1 mole of H_2SO_4

Moles of acid used in titration = $12.3 \div 1000 \times 0.1 = 0.001\,23$

Moles of NaOH in the $25\,cm^3$ sample $= 0.00123 \times 2 = 0.002\,46$

Concentration of NaOH in moles/ $dm^3 = 0.002\,46 \div 25 \times 1000$

$$= 0.0984\,mol\,dm^{-3}$$

Notes

1. The choice of indicator depends upon the relative strength of reagents being titrated, for example:

Combination of reagents	Indicator
strong acid–strong base	phenolphthalein
strong acid–weak base	methyl orange
weak acid–strong base	phenolphthalein
weak acid–weak base	no reliable indicator

2. The following mathematical expression applies to all exercises of the type described here:

$$M_1V_1 \div n_1 = M_2V_2 \div n_2$$

where M = concentration of reagent in mol dm^{-3},

V = volume/ cm^3 of the reagent used in the titration and

n = stoichiometric coefficient of the reagent in the balanced chemical equation.

The numbers 1 and 2 refer to the two reagents.

Here is the above calculation using this expression:

$$M_2 \times 25 \div 2 = 0.1 \times 12.3 \div 1$$

$$M_2 = 0.1 \times 12.3 \times 2 \div (25 \times 1) = 0.0984\,mol\,dm^{-3}$$

4.10 Determination of the relative atomic mass of magnesium

Magnesium turnings
Spatula
Scrap paper
Hydrochloric acid (2 mol dm^{-3})
Sodium hydroxide solution
   (2 mol dm^{-3})
Phenolphthalein indicator solution
Distilled water
Teat pipette (dropper)

Conical flask (250 cm^3)
Glass funnel
Pipette (25 cm^3)
Pipette filler
Burette (50 cm^3)
Bunsen burner
Tripod and gauze
Top-pan balance
Eye protection

Safety Hydrochloric acid at this concentration is irritant. Sodium hydroxide is corrosive. Phenolphthalein is a purgative and in a highly flammable solvent. Magnesium turnings are highly flammable. Eye protection is essential.

Method

1. Weigh out 0.6 g of magnesium turnings into the conical flask.
2. Put the funnel in the neck of the flask and add 50 cm³ (two 25 cm³ pipette measures) of 2 mol dm⁻³ hydrochloric acid.
3. Keep the funnel in place and warm the mixture on a tripod and gauze over a Bunsen burner until one drop changes the colour of the indicator.
4. When cool, wash both the top and under sides of the funnel with distilled water and collect the washings in the conical flask.
5. Add three drops of indicator solution, swirl the flask to mix and titrate the mixture against 2 mol dm⁻³ sodium hydroxide solution from the burette.
6. You know how much acid was added, you know how much acid remained after the reaction so you can find how much acid had reacted with the magnesium. This is an example of a back titration.

   You also know how much magnesium was present so you can calculate the relative atomic mass of magnesium by considering the stoichiometry of the reactions involved.

Sample results

Volume of NaOH needed to neutralise the mixture = 25.0 cm³

Calculations

Moles of NaOH used in the titration = 25.0 ÷ 1000 × 2 = 0.05

From equation:

$HCl + NaOH \rightarrow NaCl + H_2O$

Number of moles of unreacted HCl in the mixture = 0.05

Number of moles of HCl added to the Mg = 50 ÷ 1000 × 2 = 0.1

Number of moles of HCl which reacted with the Mg = 0.1 – 0.05 = 0.05

From equation:

$Mg + 2HCl \rightarrow MgCl_2 + H_2$

2 moles of HCl reacts with 1 mole of Mg so 0.05 moles reacts with 0.025 moles of Mg

0.025 moles of Mg = 0.6 g so 1 mole = 0.6 ÷ 0.025 = 24.0 g

Relative atomic mass of magnesium = 24

Note

The funnel in the conical flask is necessary to catch the spray from the reaction and this must be washed back into the mixture otherwise the loss of material in the spray will affect the titration result.

4.11 Analysis of common household bleaches

Measuring cylinder ($10\,cm^3$)
Blue Quink ink solution diluted 1+19
   with distilled water
Assorted household bleaches diluted
   1+39 with distilled water

Test-tubes
Teat pipette(dropper)
Eye protection

Safety Household bleaches are irritant and some are corrosive. This is a hazard for the lab technician, but at the concentration used by the students the hazard is low.

Method

1. Using the measuring cylinder, transfer $1\,cm^3$ of bleach solution to a test-tube.

2. Add the ink one drop at a time from the dropper until the blue colour of the ink persists. Shake the mixture after the addition of each drop.

3. Count the number of drops.

4. The number of drops of ink decolorised by the bleach is a measure of its concentration. More concentrated bleach will decolorise more ink.

5. Show the results in the form of a bar chart.

Results

Bleach	Drops of ink decolorised
Domestos	13
Vortex	33
Asda thin	20
Asda thick	34
Happy shopper	30

Notes

1. Household bleaches contain sodium hypochlorite (strictly, chlorate(I)) which gives up its oxygen and decolorises the dye:

   $NaOCl + dye \rightarrow NaCl + (dye + O)$

2. An alternative method for analysing the bleach is to put 1 cm³ of bleach into dimple tile wells. Immerse the end of a piece of blue litmus paper in the bleach until 1 cm has seeped into the paper. Remove the litmus paper from the bleach and measure the time for the litmus paper to decolorise. The quicker the litmus paper decolorises, the greater the concentration of bleach.

4.12 Determination of the percentage of oxygen in air

See Figure 4.3 for apparatus.

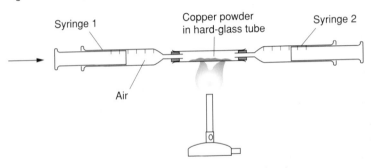

Figure 4.3 Percentage of oxygen in air.

Safety Low hazard.

Method

1. Assemble the apparatus as shown and set the volume of syringe 1 at 100 cm and syringe 2 at 0 cm³.

2. Pass the air slowly to and fro six times over the heated copper by manipulating the syringe pistons.

3. Allow the apparatus to cool (20 minutes) and read the volumes of air in each syringe.

4. The decrease in the total volume of air in the syringes is the percentage of oxygen in the air.

Sample results

	Syringe 1	Syringe 2
Start	0	100
End	0	80

Percentage of oxygen in air = 20%

Note

The hot copper powder decreases the volume of air in the syringes by reacting with oxygen present in the air:

$$2Cu + O_2 \rightarrow 2CuO$$

4.13 Determination of vitamin C concentration in fruit juice

Potassium iodate(V) solution
(0.001 mol dm^{-3})
Potassium iodide solution
(0.005 mol dm^{-3})
Sulfuric(VI) acid (1 mol dm^{-3})
Sodium thiosulfate solution
(0.01 mol dm^{-3})
Starch solution (10%)
Orange juice

Measuring cylinder (50 cm^3)
Pipette (25 cm^3) and pipette filler
Burette (50 cm^3)
Teat pipette (dropper)
White tile
Retort stand and clamp
Conical flask (250 cm^3)
Eye protection

Safety 1 mol dm^{-3} sulfuric(VI) acid is irritant.

Method

1. Using a measuring cylinder, mix 30 cm^3 of potassium iodide and 10 cm^3 of sulfuric(VI) acid in a conical flask .

2. Using the pipette and safety filler, add 25 cm^3 of potassium iodate(V) followed by 25 cm^3 of fruit juice and titrate the mixture against standard sodium thiosulfate using starch solution as the indicator.

3. Calculate the concentration of vitamin C in the fruit juice.

Sample results

Titre = 7.4 cm^3

Calculations

From equation:

$$IO_3^- + 5I^- + 6H^+ \rightarrow 3I_2 + 3H_2O \tag{1}$$

1 mol of IO_3^- produces 3 moles of I_2.

Number of moles of IO_3^- in 25 cm^3 of 0.001 mol dm^{-3} of IO_3^- solution

$$= \frac{25 \times 0.001}{1000} = 2.5 \times 10^{-5}$$

2.5×10^{-5} moles of IO_3^- produces $2.5 \times 10^{-5} \times 3$ moles of $I_2 = 7.5 \times 10^{-5}$

From equation:

$$I_2 + S_2O_3^{2-} \rightarrow S_4O_6^{2-} + 2I^- \tag{2}$$

Number of moles of I_2 found by titration with 0.01 mol dm^{-3} $Na_2S_2O_3$

$$= \frac{7.4}{1000} \times \frac{0.01}{2} = 3.7 \times 10^{-5}$$

So number of moles of I_2 used to oxidise vitamin C is the difference between the I_2 produced (equation 1) and the I_2 found by titration (equation 2):

$$= (7.5 \times 10^{-5}) - (3.7 \times 10^{-5}) = 3.8 \times 10^{-5} \text{ moles}$$

1 mole of I_2 oxidises 1 mole of vitamin C so number of moles of vitamin C in the fruit juice

$$= 3.8 \times 10^{-5} \text{ moles}$$

This was in the 25 cm^3 sample, so in 1 dm^3 there will be:

$$\frac{3.8 \times 10^{-5} \times 1000}{25} = 1.52 \times 10^{-3} \text{ mol dm}^{-3}$$

Molar mass of vitamin C = 178 g

So mass of vitamin C in 1 dm^3 of fruit juice = $1.52 \times 10^{-3} \times 178$ g

Concentration of vitamin C in the fruit juice = 0.27 g dm^{-3}

Notes

1. Iodate(V) ions react with iodide ions in the presence of sulfuric(VI) acid to produce iodine according to the following equation:

    $$IO_3^- + 5I^- + 6H^+ \rightarrow 3I_2 + 3H_2O$$

    The concentration of iodate(V) ions must be accurately known and so this reagent must be added using a pipette. The iodide and sulfuric(VI) acid need to be present in excess and so the actual concentration of these is not critical.

2. The iodine oxidises the ascorbic acid to dehydro-ascorbic acid. The equation for the reaction is:

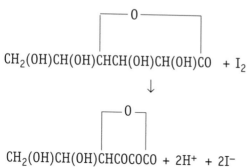

$$CH_2(OH)CH(OH)CHCH(OH)CH(OH)CO + I_2$$

$$\downarrow$$

$$CH_2(OH)CH(OH)CHCOCOCO + 2H^+ + 2I^-$$

Titrating the mixture with standard thiosulfate measures the excess iodine left after reacting with the ascorbic acid according to the following equation:

$$I_2 + 2S_2O_3^{2-} \rightarrow S_4O_6^{2-} + 2I^-$$

3. When the starch is added it forms a dark blue complex with the excess iodine.

4. The end point is reached when the starch-iodine complex becomes colourless.

4.14 Amino acid composition of casein

Reflux (see Chapter 8 Figure 8.4)
Anti-bumping granules
Paper chromatography (see
    Experiment 1.9)
Casein
Spatula
Top-pan balance
Hydrochloric acid (6 mol dm⁻³)
Liebig condenser
Measuring cylinder (10 cm³)
Filter paper and paper clip
Funnel
Beaker (250 cm³)
Evaporating basin

Propan-2-ol solution (10%)
Polythene disposable gloves
Scissors
Distilled water
Pencil
Ruler
Fine capillary tubing
Hot-air blower
Solvent mixture (butan-1-ol:
    concentrated ethanoic acid:
    distilled water :: 12 : 3 : 1)
Ninhydrin aerosol spray
Access to a fume cupboard and an oven
Eye protection

Safety $6\,mol\,dm^{-3}$ hydrochloric acid is irritant. Ninhydrin is harmful to skin and if swallowed, so this must be used in a fume cupboard and protective gloves should be worn. If a domestic hair drier has to be used, make sure that it has undergone a portable electrical appliance test and that it is electrically safe. Propan-2-ol and butan-1-ol are highly flammable and harmful by inhalation. Concentrated ethanoic acid is corrosive.

Method

A Hydrolysis of casein

1. Transfer 10 mg of casein to a $50\,cm^3$ round-bottomed flask.

2. Add $10\,cm^3$ of hydrochloric acid.

3. Add a few anti-bumping granules and then fit a vertical Liebig condenser and reflux for 20 hours. (Reflux for normal school day under supervision of lab technician; stop and re-start daily until 20 hours reflux time has passed.)

4. Transfer the mixture to an evaporating basin and evaporate to dryness on a steam bath made by boiling water in a $250\,cm^3$ beaker. The evaporating basin sits on top of the beaker.

5. Dissolve the residue in warm distilled water and evaporate to dryness again.

6. Dissolve the residue in $1\,cm^3$ of propan-2-ol solution.

B Separation and identification of amino acids

1. Wearing disposable gloves, cut a strip of filter paper to fit a gas jar.

2. Rule a fine pencilled line 1.5 cm from the bottom of the strip and mark its mid point.

3. Using a fine capillary tube, place one drop of hydrolysed protein solution to the mid point of the pencilled line until a wetted spot of 5 mm is obtained.

4. Dry the spot with a hot-air blower and repeat the application twice.

5. Roll the filter paper into a cylinder and fasten it at the top with a paper clip to hold it together.

6. Add $10\,cm^3$ of solvent to the gas jar and lower the filter-paper cylinder into the solvent, taking care not to immerse the sample spot or any part of it, and close the gas jar with a ground-glass cover.

7. When the solvent has nearly reached the top of the filter paper, remove the filter paper from the gas jar, mark the solvent front and hang it up to dry.

8. When the filter paper is dry (wear disposable gloves), spray it with ninhydrin in a fume cupboard, allow it to dry and then heat it in an oven set at 110 °C for 5 minutes. The amino acids show up as reddish purple patches.

9. Work out the retention factors (R_f values) by dividing the distances the individual amino acids travel by the distance the solvent front has travelled and identify them from the information given below:

Amino acid	R_f value	Amino acid	R_f value
Glycine	0.26	Alanine	0.38
Valine	0.60	Leucine	0.73
Isoleucine	0.72	Serine	0.27
Threonine	0.35	Aspartic acid	0.24
Asparagine	0.19	Glutamic acid	0.30
Cysteine	0.07	Methionine	0.55
Lycine	0.14	Arginine	0.20
Phenylalanine	0.68	Tyrosine	0.45
Tryptophan	0.50	Histidine	0.20
Proline	0.43		

Notes

1. A few anti-bumping granules will facilitate a smooth reflux.

2. Refluxing the mixture hydrolyses the peptide bonds and converts the amino acids in the protein to amino acid hydrochlorides.

4.15 Stoichiometry of the copper amine complex ion

Pipettes (10 and 25 cm³)
Pipette filler
Copper(II) sulfate(VI) solution
  (0.1 mol dm⁻³)
Ammonium hydroxide solution
  (1 mol dm⁻³)
Hydrochloric acid (0.01 mol dm⁻³)
Sodium hydroxide solution
  (0.01 mol dm⁻³)

Two separating funnels (100 cm³)
Trichloromethane
Disposable polythene gloves
Access to a fume cupboard
Retort stand and clamp
Burette (50 cm³)
Phenolphthalein indicator
Conical flask (100 cm³)
Eye protection

Safety Trichloromethane is harmful, irritating to skin and a category 3 carcinogen. It must be used in an efficient fume cupboard. Phenophthalein is a purgative and in a highly flammable solvent.

Method

1. Using a pipette, mix 25 cm^3 of 0.1 mol dm^{-3} copper(II) sulfate(VI) and 1 mol dm^{-3} ammonium hydroxide solutions.

2. Solvent extract the unreacted ammonium hydroxide by adding 25 cm^3 of trichloromethane with a pipette, shake the mixture and support the separating funnel in a clamp and stand while the phases separate.

3. Using a pipette, withdraw 10 cm^3 of the trichloromethane layer and transfer it to another separating funnel. Back extract the ammonium hydroxide by adding 25 cm^3 of 0.01 mol dm^{-3} hydrochloric acid and shake. Allow the phases to separate.

4. Using a pipette, withdraw 10 cm^3 of the aqueous layer and transfer it to a conical flask. Titrate against 0.01 mol dm^{-3} sodium hydroxide solution using phenolphthalein indicator.

Sample results

Titre = 5.2 cm^3

Calculation

Number of moles of NaOH in 5.2 cm^3 of 0.01 mol dm^{-3} NaOH solution
= 5.2 ÷ 1000 × 0.01 = 5.2 × 10^{-5}
From equation:

$$HCl + NaOH \rightarrow NaCl + H_2O$$

Number of moles of unreacted HCl in 10 cm^3 = 5.2 × 10^{-5}

So 25 cm^3 contains 5.2 × 10^{-5} × 25 ÷ 10 = 1.3 × 10^{-4} mol

Moles of HCl added to back extract the NH$_4$OH

= 25 ÷ 1000 × 0.01 = 2.5 × 10^{-4}

Moles of HCl which reacted = (2.5 × 10^{-4}) − (1.3 × 10^{-4}) = 1.2 × 10^{-4}

From equation:

$$HCl + NH_4OH \rightarrow NH_4Cl + H_2O$$

Moles of NH_3 in $10\,cm^3$ of the organic layer $= 1.2 \times 10^{-4}$

so in $25\,cm^3$ there are $1.2 \times 10^{-4} \times 25 \div 10\,mol = 3.0 \times 10^{-4}\,mol$

Partition coefficients are given in terms of molar concentrations. The partition coefficient for NH_3 between $CHCl_3$ and water is 1:25.

Concentration of NH_3 in the organic layer
$= 3.0 \times 10^{-4} \times 1000 \div 25 = 0.012\,mol\ dm^{-3}$

So uncomplexed NH_3 in the aqueous layer
$= 25 \times 0.012\,mol\,cm^{-3} = 0.3\,mol\ dm^{-3}$

Total volume of the aqueous layer $= 50\,cm^3$

So moles of NH_3 in $50\,cm^3 = 50 \div 1000 \times 0.3 = 0.015$

Total number of moles of uncomplexed NH_3
= moles in aqueous layer + moles in organic layer
$= 0.015 + 3 \times 10^{-4} = 0.0153$

Moles of NH_3 added $= 25 \div 1000 \times 1 = 0.025$

Moles complexed $= 0.025 - 0.01513 = 0.0099$

Moles of $Cu = 25 \div 1000 \times 0.1 = 0.0025$

Ratio of $Cu : NH_3 = 0.0025 : 0.0099 = 1 : 3.9$ or $1 : 4$

Note

The results show that the reaction between Cu^{2+} ions and ammonia is:
$$Cu^{2+} + 4NH_3 \rightarrow [Cu(NH_3)_4]^{2+}$$

4.16 Cation exchange capacity of soil

Air-dried soil (<2 mm particle size)

Leaching solution made up by mixing $1750\,cm^3$ of a solution of 95% ethanol, $280\,cm^3$ of distilled water and $1\,cm^3$ of $2\,mol\ dm^{-3}$ ammonium hydroxide solution ('alcohol reagent ')

Boric acid solution (4%)

Standard hydrochloric acid ($0.1\,mol\ dm^{-3}$)

Magnesium oxide powder

Graduated volumetric flask ($200\,cm^3$)

Leaching tube ($0.5\,m$ of $25\,mm$ glass tubing fitted with a bung and $5\,cm$ of glass capillary tube)

Silver sand

Filter paper

Scissors

Beaker ($400\,cm^3$)

Burette ($50\,cm^3$)

Indicator ($0.1\,g$ of bromocresol green in $1.5\,cm^3$ of $0.1\,mol\ dm^{-3}$ NaOH and made up to $100\,cm^3$ with distilled water)

Top-pan balance

Spatula

Retort stand and clamp

Steam distillation apparatus with the
delivery tube connected to a glass
funnel

Distilled water

Measuring cylinder (50 cm^3)

Eye protection

Safety **Take care not to scald yourself with the steam. Take the soil
sample from uncontaminated areas, i.e. no dog faeces. Wash hands
after handling soil. Ethanol is highly flammable.**

Method

1. Cut a 5 cm diameter disc of filter paper to cover the bung of the
   leaching tube and support the tube vertically in a retort stand and
   clamp (see Figure 4.4).

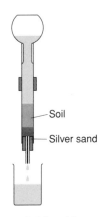

Soil

Silver sand

Figure 4.4 Leaching soil.

2. Add 10 g of silver sand to the leaching tube followed by 25 g of air-
   dried soil.

3. Fill the graduated volumetric flask to the mark with ammonium
   ethanoate solution and invert into the top of the leaching tube.

4. Collect the leachate in a beaker and discard the leachate.

5. Leach the soil again with 200 cm^3 of alcohol reagent and discard this
   leachate also.

6. Transfer the leached soil to a 500 cm^3 distillation flask. Add 2 g of
   magnesium oxide powder together with 50 cm^3 of distilled water and
   steam distil into a 400 cm^3 beaker containing 50 cm^3 of boric acid

solution with five drops of indicator added. Continue the distillation until the boric acid solution has doubled in volume to $100\,cm^3$.

7. Titrate the boric acid solution against standard hydrochloric acid.

8. Calculate the cation exchange capacity of the soil.

Sample results

Titre = $39.2\,cm^3$

From equation:

$$NH_4OH + HCl \rightarrow NH_4Cl + H_2O$$

Moles of NH_4^+ = $39.2 \div 1000 \times 0.1 = 0.00392$

Moles of cation exchange sites/$100\,g$ of soil = 0.016

Cation exchange capacity of the soil = $16\,milliequivalents$ %.

Notes

1. Ammonium ions in the ammonium ethanoate solution exchange for cations held on the clay-humus complex of the soil during the first leaching:

   $$(Clay\text{-}humus)^- M^+ + NH_4^+ \rightarrow (Clay\text{-}humus)^-NH_4^+ + M^+$$

2. Leaching with the alcohol reagent washes out the ammonium ions which have not exchanged with the soil.

3. The magnesium ions from the magnesium oxide liberate the ammonium ions from the exchange sites in the soil by ion exchange:

   $$(Clay\text{-}humus)^-NH_4^+ + Mg^{2+} \rightarrow (Clay\text{-}humus)^{2-}Mg^{2+} + NH_4^+$$

4. The magnesium oxide, being basic, also liberates ammonia from the ammonium ions:

   $$2NH_4^+ + O^{2-} \rightarrow 2NH_3 + H_2O$$

5. Ammonia is carried out of the mixture by forming hydrogen-bonds with steam:

The ammonia is collected in boric acid as an ammonia-boric acid co-ordination complex (see Figure 4.5).

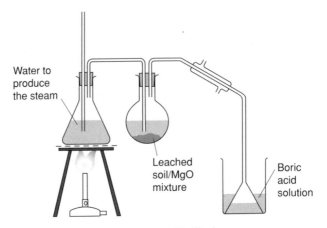

Figure 4.5 Steam distillation.

6. The colour of the indicator changes from yellow to blue.

7. The end point of the titration is reached when the indicator changes from blue to yellow.

9. Cation exchange capacity of soil is usually expressed as milli-equivalents %.

5 COLORIMETRY

The fundamental principle of all colorimetry is that the absorption of light by a coloured solution is directly proportional to its mole concentration (Beer and Lambert's law). Colorimetric analysis is usually done by adding a reagent to a solution of a particular element so that a colour is produced and then the intensity of the colour is matched with the colour of similarly treated solutions of known concentrations of that element. Colour matching can be done visually but the use of a colorimeter gives more precise results.

5.1 Building an inexpensive colorimeter

Theory

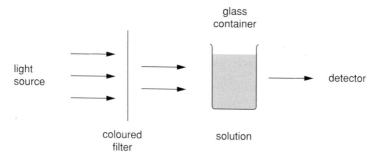

Figure 5.1 Principle of a colorimeter.

An inexpensive but effective colorimeter can be built using a light-dependent resistor (LDR) incorporated into a standard Wheatstone bridge circuit (see Figure 5.2). A torch bulb (a standard incandescent 'pea' bulb as used in common hand torches) is used as the light source. The resistance of a LDR decreases with increasing light intensity because the light falling on the semiconductor layer in the device creates extra electron hole pairs which increase its conductivity. This changes the balance of resistance in the bridge which in turn changes the current flowing through the bridge which can be measured using a milliammeter. The current imbalance in the bridge is therefore proportional to the intensity of the light detected by the LDR. One of the resistors in the bridge circuit is variable so that the balance of resistance in the bridge can be adjusted. The values for the fixed resistors have been chosen so that the range of the variable resistor covers the range of the LDR.

Many coloured solutions have their highest absorbence peaks in the visible part of the electromagnetic spectrum which corresponds to the complementary colour of the solution. Light of the appropriate wavelength is provided by placing an optical filter made of coloured gelatine set in a 35 mm photographic slide mount between the light source and the detector. The solution being tested is placed in a $50\,cm^3$ beaker between the optical filter and the LDR. The filter is supported in a slot made from 5 mm cross-sectional wooden strips glued to the base board. A V-shape using similar wooden strips, also glued to the base board, ensures that the beaker is placed in the same position each time. The complete assembly needs to be built into a lightproof box with external access terminals for connecting the ammeter and power supply so that only light from the bulb is detected by the LDR.

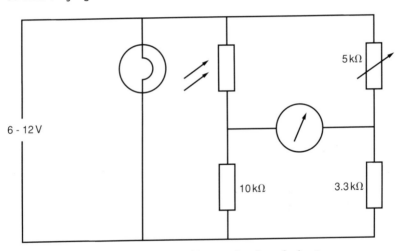

Figure 5.2 Circuit diagram for the colorimeter.

Building the colorimeter

An exploded view of the colorimeter is shown in Figure 5.3. All of the components should be mounted on a base board of 3 mm ply wood and the whole assembly enclosed in a cardboard box ($10\,cm \times 20\,cm \times 10\,cm$) with a lid to exclude daylight. Paint the interior surfaces of the box with matt black paint or line it with black sugar paper to prevent internal reflection of light off the sides of the box. Use panel pins and balsa cement (e.g. Uhu) to secure the two upright boards. Glue the wooden strips for holding the filter and for forming the V-shape in place with Uhu. Drill two small holes for the LDR and bulb-holder contacts, and mount the LDR with Uhu and the bulb holder with small nuts and bolts.

The four access terminals and the variable resistor should be mounted on the sides of the box. You can use a scalpel with a pointed blade to cut the holes. Use insulated wire for making the electrical connections. All joints should be soldered.

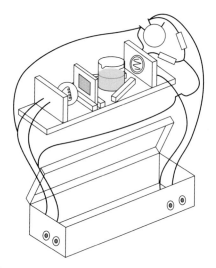

Figure 5.2 Exploded view of the colorimeter.

Using the colorimeter

1. Connect 6 V dc and a milliammeter (full scale deflection = 1 mA) or a micro-ammeter (full-scale deflection = 100 μA) as required to the appropriate terminals and switch on.

2. Place the appropriate optical filter in the light path.

3. Fill a 50 cm³ beaker with distilled water and place it in the V-shape on the base board and close the lid of the box. Do not use a graduated beaker because the graduation marks will scatter the light.

4. Using the variable resistor, adjust the resistance so that the milli-ammeter reads 1 mA.

5. Replace the distilled water in the beaker with the solution under test, close the lid of the box and record the milliammeter reading.

5.2 Colorimetric determination of plant-available soil phosphorus

Colorimeter fitted with a red filter

Sodium hydrogencarbonate solution (0.5 mol dm^{-3})

Ammonium molybdate solution acidified with sulfuric(VI) acid (25 g dm^{-3} including 350 cm^3 of concentrated H_2SO_4 /dm^3) (See Note 3.)

Sulfuric(VI) acid (1 mol dm^{-3})

Ascorbic acid solution (15 per cent w/v)

Conical flask (100 cm^3) with bung

Filter paper and funnel

Six beakers (100 cm^3)

Volumetric flask (100 cm^3)

Distilled water

Bunsen burner

Tripod and gauze

Four burettes (50 cm^3)

Measuring cylinder (50 cm^3)

Pipette (5 cm^3)

Pipette filler

Activated charcoal

Potassium dihydrogen phosphate(V) solution (4.39 g dm^{-3} KH$_2$PO$_4$)

2 mm sieve

Small block of wood

Top-pan balance

Spoon spatula

Beaker tongs

Eye protection

Sample of soil collected from safe area, i.e. not contaminated with dog faeces

Safety The ammonium molybdate is harmful and the reagent is corrosive due to the sulfuric(VI) acid it contains. 1 mol dm^{-3} sulfuric(VI) acid is irritant. Use the pipette filler to fill the pipette. Do not suck up solutions in a pipette by mouth. Wash hands after handling soil.

Method

A. Extraction of plant-available soil phosphorus

1. Spread out a sample of fresh soil on a sheet of polythene until air-dry.

2. Transfer the dry soil to the sieve, crush the soil lumps with the block of wood and collect the crumbs which pass through.

3. Weigh out 5 g of air-dry soil, <2 mm, into a conical flask and add 2 level spatula measures of activated charcoal.

4. Using the measuring cylinder, add 50 cm^3 of sodium hydrogencarbonate solution, stopper the flask and shake intermittently for 15 minutes.

5. Filter the mixture and retain the filtrate which should be colourless.

B. Analysis of the extract

1. Set up three burettes, one for each of: dilute sulfuric(VI) acid, ammonium molybdate reagent, and ascorbic acid solution.

2. Using the pipette and a pipette filler, transfer $5\,cm^3$ of the extract to a beaker.

3. Add $1\,cm^3$ of dilute sulfuric(VI) acid to expel the carbon dioxide.

4. Using the measuring cylinder add $35\,cm^3$ of distilled water.

6. Add $4\,cm^3$ of ammonium molybdate reagent followed by $1\,cm^3$ of ascorbic acid solution.

7. Heat to boiling on the tripod and gauze over the Bunsen burner. The solution should turn blue.

8. Use beaker tongs to remove the beaker from the tripod and gauze and, when cool, quantitatively transfer the solution to a $100\,cm^3$ volumetric flask, dilute to volume, stopper the flask and invert to mix.

9. Read the optical density in terms of current/mA using the colorimeter fitted with a red filter.

10. Transpose the optical density to phosphorus concentration using a calibration graph and calculate the concentration of phosphorus in the soil.

C. Calibration

1. Dilute the $4.39\,g\,dm^{-3}$ KH_2PO_4 solution $1/100$ with distilled water using a $5\,cm^3$ pipette and a $500\,cm^3$ volumetric flask and fill a fourth burette with the diluted solution. This solution contains $10\,\mu gP/cm^3$.

2. Add 0, 1, 2, 3, 4 and $5\,cm^3$ of the 10 $\mu gP/cm^3$ solution to each of six $100\,cm^3$ beakers and add $5\,cm^3$ of sodium hydrogencarbonate solution.

3. Add $1\,cm^3$ of dilute sulfuric(VI) acid to expel the carbon dioxide.

4. Add $35\,cm^3$ of distilled water followed by $4\,cm^3$ of ammonium molybdate and $1\,cm^3$ of ascorbic acid.

5. Heat to boiling on the tripod and gauze over the Bunsen burner and remove it from the tripod and gauze using tongs. Allow to cool.

6. Quantitatively transfer the solutions to $100\,cm^3$ volumetric flasks, dilute to volume with distilled water and mix.

7. Read the optical density in terms of current/mA and plot line graph of μgP on the x-axis and current/mA on the y-axis.

Sample results

B. Soil analysis

Current/mA = 0.68

C. Calibration

μgP	Current/mA
0	1.00
10	0.80
20	0.64
30	0.50
40	0.41
50	0.30

Calculation

0.68 mA corresponds to 17.5 μgP. This was in 5 cm^3 of extract so in 50 cm^3 there are 175 μgP.

50 cm^3 of sodium hydrogencarbonate solution extracted the phosphorus from 5 g of soil so 1 g of soil contains 175/5 = 35 μgP.

The concentration of plant-available phosphorus in the soil = 35 ppm, i.e. double the μgP transposed from the mA reading = ppmP in the soil.

Notes

1. Phosphorus is absorbed by plants in the form of the phosphate(V) ion. Phosphate extracted from soil using sodium hydrogencarbonate gives a very good indication of the plant-available phosphorus in soil. Soil can be classified as low, medium or high according to the following P analysis:

Soil P/ppm	P status
<15	low
15 – 35	medium
>35	high

Soil phosphate extracted with 0.5 mol dm^{-3} sodium hydrogencarbonate gives a reliable measure of the total phosphate which is available to plants. The method of analysis for phosphate in the extract was developed by Fogg and Wilkinson, *Analyst*, 83, p. 406. The organic matter in many soils produces a coloured extract which interferes with the test and this is overcome by adding activated charcoal to the soil/extractant mixture. The organic substances become adsorbed onto the surface of the charcoal particles and this decolorises the extract.

2. Soil samples are best taken with a 22.5 cm cheese auger but, if one is not available, use a spade to take out a spit to the depth of the blade. Then take a sliver of soil from the side of the spit. Take a 2.5 cm width sample of the whole length of the sliver.

3. The ammonium molybdate reagent is best prepared by dissolving 25 g of $(NH_4)_6Mo_7O_{24}.4H_2O$ in 250 cm^3 of distilled water in a 400 cm^3 beaker, warming if necessary. Add 250 cm^3 of distilled water to another 400 cm^3 beaker and stand it in a bowl of cold water. Slowly add 325 cm^3 of concentrated sulfuric(VI) acid whilst gently stirring the solution with a glass rod (care! exothermic). When both solutions are cold add the diluted sulfuric(VI) acid to the ammonium molybdate and then quantitatively transfer the mixture to a 1 dm^3 volumetric flask. Dilute to volume with distilled water, stopper the flask and invert to mix. This reagent should be stored in a dark-coloured bottle in the refrigerator when not in use.

4. I have set this activity as an ecology assignment at A-level to investigate the relationship between the concentration of phosphorus in soil and the distribution of stinging nettles. Students sampled the soil from within and without 10 separate areas of stinging nettles. They analysed the soil for plant-available phosphorus and carried out a statistical analysis of the data. Soil within the beds of nettles contained a significantly higher concentration of phosphorus than did soil outside the nettle beds.

5.3 Colorimetric determination of manganese in steel

Colorimeter fitted with a green filter
6 V dc power supply
Ammeter (full scale deflection = 1 mA)
Plain beaker (50 cm^3)
Metal file
Steel rod
Spatula
Scrap paper
Vice

Seven beakers (100 cm^3)
Eight volumetric flasks (100 cm^3) with stoppers
Nitric(V) acid (2 mol dm^{-3})
Phosphoric(V) acid (1 mol dm^{-3})
Potassium iodate(VII)
Funnel
Top-pan balance
Measuring cylinder (10 cm^3)

Manganese sulfate(VI) solution
    (10.14 g dm^{-3} MnSO$_4$.4H2O)

Pipette (10 cm^3)

Pipette filler

Burette (50 cm^3)

Distilled water

Bunsen burner

Tripod and gauze

Beaker tongs

Eye protection

Safety 2 mol dm^{-3} **nitric(V) is corrosive. 1 mol dm^{-3} phosphoric(V) acid is irritant. Potassium iodate(VII) is an oxidising agent. Use the pipette filler to fill the pipette. Do not suck up solutions in a pipette by mouth.**

Method

A. Extraction of manganese from steel

1. Secure the steel rod in the vice, use the file to produce filings and collect them on the piece of scrap paper.

2. Weigh out 0.1 g of filings into a beaker.

3. Using a measuring cylinder, measure out 10 cm^3 of nitric(V) acid and add it to the steel filings.

4. In a fume cupboard, warm the mixture on a tripod and gauze over a Bunsen burner. All of the filings should dissolve to produce a pale yellow solution.

5. Add 10 cm^3 of phosphoric(V) acid followed by 20 cm^3 of distilled water. Add 0.1 g of KIO$_4$ and heat the solution to boiling. The solution should turn purple due to the formation of potassium manganate(VII).

6. When cool, quantitatively transfer the solution to a volumetric flask and dilute to volume with distilled water.

7. Stopper the flask and invert to mix.

8. Measure the optical density in terms of current/mA using the colorimeter fitted with a green filter.

9. Transpose the optical density to manganese concentration using a calibration graph and calculate the percentage of manganese in the original sample of steel.

B Colorimeter calibration

1. Dilute the 10.14 g/dm^3 MnSO$_4$.4H$_2$O standard solution 1/10 by transferring, with a pipette, 10 cm^3 to a 100 cm^3 volumetric flask and dilute to volume with distilled water and mix. This solution contains 0.25 mg Mn/cm^3.

2. Using a burette, add 0, 1, 2, 3, 4, 5 and $6\,cm^3$ of the $0.25\,mg\ Mn/cm^3$ solution to each of seven beakers.

3. Add $10\,cm^3$ of nitric(V) acid followed by $10\,cm^3$ of phosphoric(V) acid.

4. Add $20\,cm^3$ of distilled water followed by $0.1\,g$ of KIO_4 and heat to boiling.

5. When cool, quantitatively transfer the contents of the beakers to each of seven $100\,cm^3$ volumetric flasks and dilute to volume. Stopper the flasks and invert to mix the contents.

6. Measure the optical density of the solutions in terms of current/mA using the colorimeter fitted with a green filter.

7. Plot a line graph of mg of Mn on the x-axis and current/mA on the y-axis.

Sample results

A. Analysis of steel

Current/mA $= 0.59$

B. Calibration

Mn/mg	Current/mA
0.00	0.78
0.25	0.70
0.50	0.56
0.75	0.46
1.00	0.40
1.25	0.28
1.50	0.20

Calculation

Using the calibration curve, $0.59\,mA$ corresponds to $0.48\,mg$ of Mn. This was extracted from $0.1\,g$ ($100\,mg$) of steel so the concentration of Mn in the steel $= 0.48\,mg/100\,mg$ or 0.48%.

Notes

1. The equations for the reactions:

$$Mn + 4HNO_3 \rightarrow Mn(NO_3)_2 + 2NO_2 + 2H_2O$$

$$2Mn^{2+} + 5IO_4^- + 3H_2O \rightarrow 2MnO_4^- + 5IO_3^- + 6H^+$$

Phosphoric(V) acid needs to be included to prevent the iron from interfering with the analysis. The optical density of the colour due to the manganate(VII) ions is proportional to its molecular concentration. The colorimeter needs to be fitted with a green filter which is complementary to the colour of the solution.

2. It is easier to fill a burette from a beaker with a spout than directly from a volumetric flask.

3. Remove the beaker containing the hot solution from the tripod and gauze using beaker tongs.

4. Wash out the beaker with a small quantity of the solution to be tested beforehand to avoid contamination by the previous sample.

5. Always use the same beaker for measuring the optical density of the solution and always place it in the same position with the spout in the same direction every time. If this is not done there will be errors caused by the different orientation of the beaker scattering light differently.

5.4 Colorimetric determination of glucose using Benedict's reagent

Colorimeter fitted with a red filter
Glucose solutions (0.2, 0.4, 0.6, 0.8 and 1.0%)
Benedict's reagent, prepare fresh (see Note 4)
Centrifuge
Centrifuge tubes (15 × 100 mm)
Measuring cylinders (10 cm^3 and 20 cm^3)

Beaker of boiling water (250 cm^3)
Ammonia solution (s.g. 0.88)
Sulfuric(VI) acid (1 mol dm^{-3})
Hydrogen peroxide (10 vol)
Distilled water
Volumetric flasks (100 cm^3)
Eye protection

Safety Sulfuric(VI) acid is irritant. 0.88 ammonia is corrosive and produces a toxic gas. Ammonia can cause asthma attacks in susceptible people so work in a well ventilated room. Ensure that the centrifuge conforms to modern safety standards.

Method

1. Using the measuring cylinder, transfer 1 cm^3 of glucose solution to a centrifuge tube.

2. Add 10 cm^3 of Benedict's solution and place the tube in a beaker of boiling water for 5 minutes.

3. Transfer the tube to a centrifuge and spin down the precipitated copper(I) oxide.

4. Discard the supernatant, wash the precipitate by adding distilled water, centrifuge again and discard the supernatant.

5. Add 4 cm^3 of sulfuric(VI) acid followed by 2 cm^3 of hydrogen peroxide and warm gently over a Bunsen flame to dissolve the precipitate.

6. Cool and add 4 cm^3 of ammonia solution and then quantitatively transfer the mixture to a 100 cm^3 volumetric flask.

7. Dilute to volume with distilled water, stopper the flask and invert several times to mix.

8. Transfer the solution to the beaker of the colorimeter and measure the optical density in terms of the current flowing.

9. Repeat the procedure for all glucose solutions and plot a line graph of percentage glucose on the x-axis and current/μA on the y-axis.

Sample results

% Glucose	Current/μA
0	100
0.2	84
0.4	67
0.6	51
0.8	35
1.0	18

Notes

1. Use distilled water as a blank to set the ammeter of the colorimeter to full-scale deflection.

2. The hydrogen peroxide oxidises the Cu(I) to Cu(II).

3. The addition of ammonia solution enhances the intensity of the colour by forming the $[Cu(NH_3)_4]^{2+}$ ion.

4. Benedict's reagent: prepare fresh by dissolving 100 g of sodium carbonate and 173 g of sodium citrate in 600 cm^3 of distilled water, filter and dilute to 850 cm^3. Dissolve 17.3 g of copper(II) sulfate(VI) in 150 cm^3 of distilled water, and mix the two solutions.

5.5 Colorimetric determination of iron in breakfast cereal

Colorimeter fitted with a blue filter
Concentrated sulfuric(VI) acid
Sodium hydroxide solution
  (2 mol dm^{-3})
Hydrogen peroxide (100 vol)
Teat pipette (dropper)
Measuring cylinder (10 cm^3)
Beaker (100 cm^3)
Bunsen burner
Tripod and gauze
Heat-resistant gloves
Distilled water
Volumetric flask (100 cm^3) with
  stopper

Funnel
Iron(II) ammonium sulfate(VI)
  solution (7.00 g dm^{-3}
  Fe(NH$_4$)$_2$(SO$_4$)$_2$.6H$_2$O)
1,10-phenanthroline reagent (1.5% of
  the hydrate in ethanol)
Hydroxy-ammonium chloride (10%)
Top-pan balance
Spatula
Three burettes (50 cm^3)
Weetabix breakfast cereal
Safety goggles

Safety Concentrated sulfuric(VI) acid, 2 mol dm^{-3} sodium hydroxide and 100 vol hydrogen peroxide are all corrosive. The concentrated acid needs to be heated and this must be done in a safe place where it cannot be knocked over. The beaker of hot acid must be handled with great care. Hydroxy-ammonium chloride is harmful if swallowed. 1,10-phenanthroline is toxic by inhalation, skin contact or if swallowed and is in a highly flammable solvent. Safety goggles, i.e. not safety spectacles, are essential.

Method

A. Extraction of iron

1. Crumble the Weetabix in a polythene bag and weigh out 0.2 g into a 100 cm^3 beaker.

2. Using a measuring cylinder, add 10 cm^3 of concentrated sulfuric(VI) acid.

3. Very carefully and in a fume cupboard, warm the mixture on a tripod and gauze over the Bunsen burner for about 5 minutes to digest the Weetabix. The mixture turns black and oily.

4. Wearing heat-resistant gloves, remove the beaker from the tripod and gauze. Whilst still hot and swirling the beaker, add hydrogen peroxide dropwise until the solution becomes colourless. Allow to cool to room temperature.

5. Using a funnel, quantitatively transfer the solution to a 100 cm^3 volumetric flask.

6. Adjust the pH to between 1.5 and 3.0 by adding 2 mol dm^{-3} sodium hydroxide solution (5 cm^3) using a measuring cylinder.

7. Set up two burettes and fill one with hydroxy-ammonium chloride solution and the other with phenanthroline reagent.

8. Add 2 cm^3 of hydroxy-ammonium chloride solution followed by 1 cm^3 of phenanthroline reagent, mix by swirling the flask and set aside for 30 minutes for the colour to develop.

9. Dilute to volume with distilled water, stopper the flask and invert to mix.

10. Read the optical density in terms of current/mA and transpose the reading to µgFe using a calibration curve.

11. Calculate the concentration of iron in the Weetabix.

B. Calibration

1. Dilute the 7.00 g dm^{-3} iron(II) ammonium sulfate(VI) solution 1/100 with distilled water. This gives a standard solution containing 10 µgFe/cm^3.

2. Set up another burette and fill it with the diluted iron(II) ammonium sulfate(VI) solution.

3. Add 0, 1, 2, 3, 4, 5 and 6 cm^3 of 10 µgFe/cm^3 standard solution to each of seven 100 cm^3 volumetric flasks.

4. Add 2 cm^3 of hydroxy-ammonium chloride solution followed by 1 cm^3 of phenanthroline reagent, swirl the flasks to mix and set aside for 30 minutes for the colour to develop.

5. Dilute to volume with distilled water, stopper the flasks, invert them to mix and read the optical density in terms of current/mA using the colorimeter fitted with a blue filter.

6. Draw a line graph of µgFe on the x-axis and current/mA on the y-axis.

Results
A. Analysis of Weetabix
Current/mA = 0.56

B. Calibration

Fe/µg	Current/mA
0	0.80
10	0.73
20	0.65
30	0.54
40	0.48
50	0.40
60	0.35

Calculation

A current of 0.56 mA corresponds to 30 µg of iron. This was extracted from 0.2 g of Weetabix so the concentration of iron in the Weetabix was 150 µg/g or 150 ppm.

Notes

1. 1,10-phenanthroline is a bidentate ligand, three moles of which forms a chelate with one mole of Fe^{3+} ions to give an octahedral orange-red complex. The intensity of the colour is proportional to its molecular concentration. The colorimeter needs to be fitted with a blue filter which is complementary to the colour of the solution being tested.

2. Dissolve the iron(II) ammonium sulfate(VI) in cold distilled water. If you heat it, the iron(II) will oxidise to iron(III). After the salt has dissolved, add a drop of concentrated sulfuric(VI) acid to the solution before diluting to volume in order to prevent oxidation.

5.6 Stoichiometry of the copper-edta complex

Colorimeter fitted with a red filter

Two burettes (50 cm³)

Distilled water

Ten graduated volumetric flasks (100 cm³)

Copper(II) sulfate(VI) solution (0.05 mol dm⁻³)

Solution of the disodium salt of edta (0.1 mol dm⁻³)

Two retort stands and clamps

Marker pen

Safety Low hazard.

Method

1. Using the marker pen, number the flasks 1–10.

2. Using a burette, add 10 cm^3 of copper(II) sulfate(VI) solution to each flask.

3. Using the other burette, add 0, 1, 2, 3, 4, 5, 6, 7, 8, 9 and 10 cm^3 of edta solution to the flasks containing the copper(II) sulfate(VI) solution.

4. Dilute to volume with distilled water, stopper the flasks and invert them to mix. The flasks contain mixtures of Cu^{2+}:edta in the ratio of 0–2 in increments of 0.2.

5. Use the colorimeter to measure the optical density in terms of the meter reading/μA.

6. Plot a line graph of Cu^{2+}:edta ratio on the x-axis against meter reading/μA on the y-axis and deduce the stoichiometry of the Cu-edta complex.

Sample results

Cu^{2+}:edta	Meter reading/μA
0	80
0.2	70
0.4	60
0.6	48
0.8	42
1.0	31
1.2	32
1.4	32
1.6	30
1.8	32
2.0	30

Notes

1. The edta solution is in the form of the disodium salt of ethylene diamine tetraacetic acid (recommended name 1,2-bis [bis (carboxylmethyl) amine] ethane). This is a polydentate ligand which chelates with Cu^{2+} ions by forming bonds with the nitrogen atoms and also the OHs of two of the ethanoate groups:

$$\text{Na}^+\text{O}^-\text{OC} - \text{CH}_2 - \overset{\displaystyle\overset{\textstyle H-C-H}{|}}{\underset{\displaystyle\underset{\textstyle O=C}{\underset{\textstyle |}{\text{CH}_2}}}{N}} \cdots \overset{\displaystyle\overset{\textstyle C-H}{|}}{\underset{\displaystyle\underset{\textstyle O=C}{\underset{\textstyle |}{\text{CH}_2}}}{N}} - \text{CH}_2 - \text{COO}^-\text{Na}^+$$

Structure (as drawn):

```
          H              H
          |              |
       H-C ──────────── C-H
          |              |
Na⁺O⁻OC - CH₂ - N ────── N - CH₂ - COO⁻Na⁺
          |   \        / |
          CH₂   \    /   CH₂
          |      Cu      |
      O = C    /    \    O = C
          |  /        \  |
          O⁻            O⁻
```

2. The graph shows that the stoichiometry of the Cu–edta complex is 1:1 because further additions of the ligand beyond this failed to increase the optical density of the mixture.

3. Use water as a blank and adjust the colorimeter meter to full-scale deflection before reading the optical densities of the solutions.

4. Avoid contamination from the previous test by washing out the beaker with a little of the solution before measuring its optical density.

6 ACIDS, BASES and SALTS

An acid is a substance which dissolves in water to produce oxonium ions H_3O^+. Acids contain hydrogen atoms which are covalently bonded to an atom of a non-metal. When the molecule dissolves in water, the hydrogen atom dissociates from the non-metal atom and the resulting hydrogen ion attaches to a water molecule to form the oxonium ion:

$$HCl + H_2O \rightarrow H_3O^+ + Cl^-$$

The oxonium ions give the solution its acidic properties.

A base is a substance which reacts with an acid to give a salt and water as the only products. Bases are metal oxides or hydroxides. An alkali is a soluble base. When the alkali dissolves the hydroxide ions give the solution its basic properties:

$$NaOH(s) + H_2O(l) \rightarrow Na^+(aq) + OH^-(aq)$$

$$NH_3(g) + H_2O(l) \rightarrow NH_4^+(aq) + OH^-(aq)$$

The reaction between an acid and a base is called neutralisation. During neutralisation the oxonium ions and hydroxide ions react to produce water:

$$H_3O^+ + O^{2-} \rightarrow H_2O + OH^-$$

$$H_3O^+ + OH^- \rightarrow 2H_2O$$

The atom, or group of atoms, which is covalently bonded to the acidic hydrogen atom is called an acid radical, e.g. in sulfuric(VI) acid, the acid radical is the sulfate(VI) group. A salt is a substance in which a metal or an ammonium ion is ionically bonded to an acid radical. The number of acidic hydrogen atoms in a molecule is called the basicity of the acid. If all of the acidic hydrogen atoms are replaced by a metal the salt formed is neutral. If only some of them are replaced the salt is acidic because when the salt dissolves in water, the remaining hydrogen atoms will dissociate and form oxonium ions with water molecules.

The acidity or alkalinity of a solution is given by its pH. The pH scale ranges from 1–14. Acids have pH < 7, alkalis have pH > 7 and neutral solutions have a pH = 7. Substances which change colour according to pH are called pH indicators.

6.1 Extracting and testing natural indicator substances from plant material

Beetroot
Blackberries
Onion skins
Kettle of hot water
Mortar and pestle
Silver sand
Spatula

Sulfuric(VI) acid (0.1 mol dm^{-3})
Saturated calcium hydroxide solution
    (limewater)
Test-tubes
Filter paper and funnel
Eye protection

Safety Some risk of splashing.

Method

1. Take each sample of plant material in turn and place it in the mortar.

2. Add a spatula measure of silver sand and add some hot water from the kettle.

3. Grind the plant material to a pulp using the pestle and then filter the mixture and collect the filtrate in a test-tube.

4. Divide the filtrate into three equal parts and add sulfuric(VI) acid to one part, sodium chloride to another and limewater to the other part.

5. Note any colour changes that take place.

Sample results

Plant extract	Colour	
	Sulfuric(VI) acid	Limewater
Beetroot	Red	Yellow
Blackberries	Red	Black/Blue
Onion skins	Colourless	Yellow

Notes

1. Sulfuric(VI) acid is acidic and limewater is alkaline.

2. The plant material contained pH indicators which changed colour according to the pH of the solution.

6.2 Comparing the acid-base properties of metal and non-metal oxides

Sodium
Calcium
Magnesium
White phosphorus
Sulfur
Carbon
Six deflagrating spoons
Six gas jars of oxygen
Distilled water
Universal pH indicator solution

pH reference colour chart
White ceramic tile
Scalpel
Forceps
Mortar
Absorbent paper tissues
Bunsen burner
Access to fume cupboard
Safety screens
Eye protection

Safety Safety screens must be used to protect the teacher and students. Use no more than 0.5 cm cubes of sodium and phosphorus. Handle sodium with forceps to avoid contact with the moisture on the skin. White phosphorus, when dry, spontaneously ignites on exposure to air. Handle phosphorus with forceps. It must be cut up under water in a mortar. Any phosphorus fires should be flooded with water and treated with solid copper(II) sulfate(VI). The copper(II) sulfate(VI) will turn black when in contact with phosphorus. Work in a well ventilated area because oxides of phosphorus and sulfur dioxide formed from the reactions irritate the nose, throat and eyes if inhaled. Sodium is both highly flammable and corrosive. Sodium oxide is corrosive. Calcium is highly flammable and its oxide is corrosive. Magnesium is highly flammable. White phosphorus is very toxic and its oxides are corrosive. Sulfur is flammable and its oxide is toxic and corrosive. These experiments involving phosphorus and sulfur should be carried out in a fume cupboard. Oxygen is oxidising.

Method

1. Take each substance (except white phosphorus which ignites spontaneously when the water evaporates) in turn in a deflagrating spoon and hold it over a Bunsen flame until it begins to burn or is glowing red hot.

2. Quickly transfer the deflagrating spoon to a gas jar containing oxygen.

3. After the reaction has subsided, wash the deflagrating spoon with a little distilled water and collect the washings in the gas jar.

4. Remove the deflagrating spoon, close the gas jar with a lid and shake to dissolve the contents of the gas jar.

5. Test the pH of the solution using Universal indicator. Stand solution on white ceramic tile and compare with reference chart.

6. Ensure that any remaining phosphorus is burnt off in a fume cupboard before the end of term.

Sample results

Oxide	pH
Sodium oxide	14
Magnesium oxide	10
Calcium oxide	14
Sulfur dioxide	1
Phosphorus(V) oxide	3
Carbon dioxide	5

Note

The results show that metal oxides are basic and non-metal oxides are acidic.

6.3 Preparation of nitric(V) acid

Two retort stands and three clamps
Glass retort and ground glass stopper
Retort ring
Gauze
Bunsen burner
Long-necked round-bottomed flask (250 cm³)
Concentrated sulfuric(VI) acid

Potassium nitrate(V)
Top-pan balance
Litmus
Copper turnings
Measuring cylinder (25 cm³)
Access to running water
Eye protection

Safety Concentrated sulfuric(VI) acid is corrosive. Potassium nitrate(V) is an oxidising agent and can cause a fire with combustible materials. The nitric(V) acid produced is corrosive and oxidising. Safety goggles are essential. If a retort is not available it is essential to use all-glass apparatus (e.g. Quickfit) as rubber will be attacked.

Method

1. Assemble the apparatus as shown in Figure 6.1.

2. Put 10 g of potassium nitrate(V) and 18 cm³ of concentrated sulfuric(VI) acid in the retort.

3. Heat gently until the solid has dissolved and then more strongly.

4. Collect the distillate in the round-bottomed flask.

5. Test the distillate with litmus and also with copper turnings (toxic and corrosive gas produced).

Sample results

The distillate was a pale yellow mobile liquid which turned blue litmus red and reacted with copper turnings to form a dark green solution together with brown fumes.

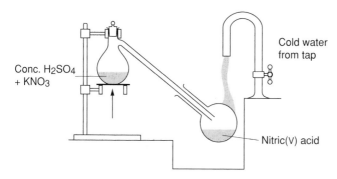

Figure 6.1 Preparation of nitric(V) acid.

Notes

1. The distillate was concentrated nitric(V) acid. The pure acid is colourless. The pale yellow colour was due to nitrogen dioxide which was formed by slight decomposition of the nitric(V) acid. The nitrogen dioxide dissolved in the nitric(V) acid turning it yellow. The nitrogen dioxide can be removed from the sample by bubbling air through it.

2. The equation for the reaction:

$$KNO_3 + H_2SO_4 \rightarrow HNO_3 + KHSO_4$$

Any metal nitrate will produce nitric(V) acid when heated with concentrated sulfuric(VI) acid.

3. The equation for the reaction between concentrated nitric(V) acid and copper turnings:

$$Cu + 4HNO_3 \rightarrow Cu(NO_3)_2 + 2NO_2 + 2H_2O$$

If the nitric(V) acid is diluted with its own volume of water then:

$$3Cu + 8HNO_3 \rightarrow 3Cu(NO_3)_2 + 2NO_2 + 4H_2O$$

6.4 Comparing the strength of acids by measuring electrical conductivity

Ammeter (0 -1 A and 0 -5 A dual range)

Graphite rods mounted in a rubber bung

Two crocodile clips

Three connecting leads with 4 mm plugs at each end

Distilled water in a beaker (100 cm^3)

25 cm^3 of a range of concentrated and diluted acids (1 mol dm^{-3}) in beakers (100 cm^3): hydrochloric acid, sulfuric(VI) acid and ethanoic acid

Absorbent paper tissues

Disposable polythene gloves

Eye protection

Safety

Acid	Concentrated	1 mol dm^{-3}
Sulfuric(VI) acid	Corrosive	Irritant
Hydrochloric acid	Corrosive	Low hazard
Ethanoic acid	Corrosive	Low hazard

Avoid contact with the skin by wearing disposable gloves when handling concentrated ethanoic acid. It continues to harm the skin even after attempts have been made to wash it off!

Method

Follow the method described in Experiment 8.1.

Sample results

Acid	Current/A
Concentrated sulfuric(VI)	0
Dilute sulfuric(VI)	1.3
Concentrated hydrochloric	0.3
Dilute hydrochloric	1.5
Concentrated ethanoic	0
Dilute ethanoic	0.6

Notes

1. Strong acids are fully ionised, weak acids are only partly ionised.
2. The greater the degree of ionisation the higher the electrical conductivity.

6.5 Comparing the electrical conductivity of hydrogen chloride dissolved in water and also in methylbenzene

Conical flask ($250\,cm^3$)
A bung to fit the flask with holes to
    take a delivery tube and a
    separating funnel
Rubber tubing
Concentrated sulfuric(VI) acid
Distilled water
Sodium chloride
Methylbenzene (toluene)
Magnesium turnings
Blue litmus solution

Aqueous ammonia ($2\,mol\,dm^{-3}$)
Two beakers ($100\,cm^3$)
Five test-tubes in a rack
Two graphite rods mounted in a bung
Two crocodile clips
Three connecting wires with 4 mm
    plugs at each end
Ammeter (0–5 A)
6 V dc power supply
Eye protection
Access to fume cupboard

Safety Methylbenzene is highly flammable and dissolves natural oils in skin. Concentrated sulfuric(VI) acid is corrosive. Work in a fume cupboard because the hydrogen chloride produced, if inhaled, irritates the eyes, nose and throat. It is also toxic and corrosive. Magnesium is highly flammable. Eye protection is essential.

Method

1. Set up the apparatus as shown in Figure 6.2.

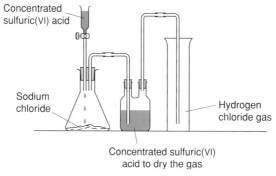

Figure 6.2 Preparation of hydrogen chloride.

85

2. Add the concentrated sulfuric(VI) acid to the sodium chloride in the conical flask and prepare solutions of hydrogen chloride in distilled water and methylbenzene by bubbling the gas through these solvents contained in $100\,cm^3$ beakers. Use a fume cupboard.

3. Connect the graphite rods in series with the ammeter and the power supply and measure the electrical conductivity of the two solutions.

4. Test each solution with litmus, magnesium turnings and aqueous ammonia.

Sample results

Test	Solution	
	Aqueous	**In methylbenzene**
Current/A	1.3	0
Litmus	red	no effect
Mg turnings	H_2 evolved	no effect
NH_4OH	-	white precipitate

Notes

1. Equation for the production of hydrogen chloride:

   $$NaCl + H_2SO_4 \rightarrow NaHSO_4 + HCl$$

2. The white precipitate obtained when the hydrogen chloride in methylbenzene was tested with aqueous ammonia was ammonium chloride and confirms the presence of hydrogen chloride in the solution.

   $$HCl + NH_4OH \rightarrow NH_4Cl + H_2O$$

3. The different properties of the two solutions shows that hydrogen chloride is covalent but ionises on contact with water:

   $$HCl + H_2O \rightarrow H_3O^+ + Cl^-$$

6.6 Preparation of a salt by reacting a metal, metal oxide or hydroxide or carbonate with an acid

Metal (magnesium, zinc or copper)

Metal oxide (magnesium, zinc or copper)

Metal hydroxide (magnesium, zinc or copper)

Metal carbonate (magnesium, zinc or copper)	Measuring cylinder ($25\,cm^3$)
	Beaker ($100\,cm^3$)
Acid ($1\,mol\,dm^{-3}$ sulfuric(VI), hydrochloric or nitric(V))	Bunsen burner
	Tripod and gauze
Retort stand and clamp	Evaporating basin
Filter paper and funnel	Absorbent paper tissue
Spatula	Eye protection

Safety $1\,mol\,dm^{-3}$ sulfuric(VI) acid is irritant. $1\,mol\,dm^{-3}$ nitric(V) acid is corrosive. Copper compounds are harmful if swallowed and are skin irritants if handled. Eye protection is essential. Risk of spitting if the solution of the salt is boiled nearly dry. Do NOT let sulfates or nitrates boil dry – hazardous gases are produced.

Method

1. Using the measuring cylinder, transfer 25 cm^3 of the acid to a beaker.

2. Add spatula measures of the metal (not much reaction with copper), metal oxide, hydroxide or carbonate until all visible signs of a reaction have stopped and the solid is present in excess.

3. Warm the mixture on a tripod and gauze over a Bunsen burner.

4. Support a filter funnel in the clamp and stand and place the evaporating basin underneath the funnel.

5. Filter the mixture through a fluted filter paper and collect the filtrate in the evaporating basin.

6. Boil the filtrate to one third of its original volume and set aside to crystallise.

7. Remove the crystals from the solution with a spatula and blot them dry with absorbent paper tissues.

Note

Use the appropriate metal or metal compound with the acid which contains the appropriate acid radical:
Hydrochloric acid is a chloride maker
Sulfuric(VI) acid is a sulfate(VI) maker
Nitric(V) acid is a nitrate(V) maker

6.7 Preparation of a soluble salt from soluble reactants

Aqueous sodium or potassium hydroxide ($2\,mol\,dm^{-3}$)

Sulfuric(VI) acid ($1\,mol\,dm^{-3}$)

Hydrochloric acid or nitric(V) acid ($2\,mol\,dm^{-3}$)

Retort stand and clamp

Burette ($50\,cm^3$)

Pipette ($25\,cm^3$)

Pipette filler

Phenolphthalein solution

Teat pipette (dropper)

Conical flask ($250\,cm^3$)

Evaporating basin

Absorbent paper tissue

Spatula

Bunsen burner

Tripod and gauze

Eye protection

Safety The alkalis are corrosive. Phenolphthalein is a purgative and in a highly flammable solvent. $1\,mol\,dm^{-3}$ sulfuric(VI) acid and $2\,mol\,dm^{-3}$ hydrochloric acid are both irritant. $2\,mol\,dm^{-3}$ nitric(V) acid is corrosive. Do not allow sulfates(IV)s (sulfites) or nitric(III)s (nitrites) to dry – hazardous gases are produced. Eye protection is essential.

Method

1. Fill the burette with acid.

2. Using the pipette and pipette filler transfer $25\,cm^3$ of sodium or potassium hydroxide to the conical flask.

3. Add a few drops of phenolphthalein solution and run in the acid from the burette whilst swirling the flask until one drop just decolorises the phenolphthalein.

4. Make a note of the burette reading.

5. Repeat steps 1 and 2 and add the same volume of acid as in step 4.

6. Pour the mixture into the evaporating basin and proceed as described in Experiment 6.6, steps 6 and 7.

Note

As for Experiment 6.6.

6.8 Preparation of soap

Measuring cylinder ($10\,cm^3$)

Aqueous sodium hydroxide solution ($4\,mol\,dm^{-3}$)

Castor oil or olive oil

Ethanol

Sodium chloride

Spoon spatula

Beaker ($250\,cm^3$)

Bunsen burner
Tripod and gauze
Glass rod

Dimple tile
Absorbent paper tissues
Safety goggles

Safety 4 mol dm^{-3} sodium hydroxide is dangerously corrosive. Ethanol is flammable and causes severe burns. The soap must not be used on naked skin because it will cause itching due to the presence of sodium hydroxide. Safety goggles (not safety specs) must be worn. Extensive frothing occurs in this experiment. The froth is highly corrosive.

Method

1. Mix 10 cm^3 each of castor oil, sodium hydroxide and ethanol in a beaker.

2. Heat gently whilst stirring with a glass rod. The mixture froths up and the ethanol vapour may catch fire so have a damp cloth or heatproof mat ready to cover the beaker if this happens.

3. When the frothing has ceased, add two rounded spatula measures of sodium chloride and stir with the glass rod. Frothing occurs again at this stage in the procedure.

4. Remove the beaker from the tripod and gauze and allow it to cool.

5. Decant off the liquid soap which appears on the surface of the mixture into the wells of the dimple tile where it will solidify on cooling.

6. The tablets of soap can be removed and blotted dry with absorbent paper tissue.

Notes

1. The equation for the reaction is:

$$CH_3(CH_2)_{14}COOH + NaOH \rightarrow CH_3(CH_2)_{14}COONa + H_2O$$

2. Soap is sodium octadecanoate (stearate) which is the sodium salt of octadecanoic (stearic) acid present in the castor oil.

3. The tablets of soap can be tested by creating a lather in distilled water.

6.9 Analysis of indigestion remedies

A variety of commercial indigestion remedies

Hydrochloric acid ($1 mol dm^{-3}$)

Sodium hydroxide solution ($1 mol dm^{-3}$)

Top-pan balance

Spatula

Pipette ($25 cm^3$)

Pipette filler

Burette ($50 cm^3$)

Phenolphthalein indicator solution

Mortar and pestle

Conical flask ($100 cm^3$)

White ceramic tile

Eye protection

Safety 1 mol dm⁻³ sodium hydroxide solution is corrosive. Phenolphthalein is a purgative and in a highly flammable solvent. Use the pipette filler to fill the pipette. Do not suck up solutions in a pipette by mouth.

Method

1. Using the mortar and pestle, crush an indigestion tablet to a powder.

2. Weigh out 1 g of the powdered tablet and transfer it to a conical flask.

3. Using a pipette with a pipette filler, add 25 cm³ of hydrochloric acid, swirl the flask and leave for five minutes to dissolve the active ingredients.

4. Add five drops of phenolphthalein indicator solution and titrate the excess acid in the mixture with sodium hydroxide solution from the burette.

5. Repeat the procedure with each indigestion remedy.

Sample results

1 g of powdered Settlers' tablet required 18.0 cm³ of sodium hydroxide solution to neutralise the excess acid in the mixture.

Calculation

From equation:

$NaOH + HCl \rightarrow NaCl + H_2O$

Moles of NaOH = moles of HCl.

From equation:

$CaCO_3 + 2HCl \rightarrow CaCl_2 + H_2O + CO_2$

1 mole of HCl $\equiv$ 0.5 moles of $CaCO_3$.

Volume of acid neutralised by 1 g of indigestion remedy

$= 25 - 18 = 7 \, cm^3$.

Converting to moles $= \dfrac{7 \times 1}{1000} = 7 \, millimoles$

Active ingredient in the indigestion remedy $= \dfrac{7}{2} = 3.5 \, millimoles/g$

Notes

1. Indigestion remedies contain calcium and magnesium carbonates as the active ingredient. These neutralise excess acid in the stomach to produce calcium and magnesium chlorides, water and carbon dioxide.

2. Indigestion remedies which contain more of the active ingredient will be more effective in neutralising excess acid in the stomach and give greater relief from indigestion.

6.10 Titration curves for strong and weak acids and alkalis

$0.1 \, mol \, dm^{-3}$ solutions of hydrochloric acid, ethanoic acid, sodium hydroxide and aqueous ammonia
Distilled water
Pipette ($25 \, cm^3$)
Pipette filler

Burette ($50 \, cm^3$)
Beaker ($100 \, cm^3$)
pH meter
pH4 and pH7 buffer solutions
Eye protection

Safety $0.1 \, mol \, dm^{-3}$ **NaOH is irritant. Use the pipette filler to fill the pipette. Do not suck up solutions in a pipette by mouth.**

Method

1. Calibrate the pH meter by immersing the electrodes in the pH4 buffer solution, swirl the beaker, and adjust the reading to 4.0. Remove the electrodes, wash with distilled water and immerse them in the pH9 buffer solution. The pH meter should read pH9.

2. Using the pipette and filler, transfer $25 \, cm^3$ of acid to the beaker and measure its pH.

3. Add the alkali, $5 \, cm^3$ at a time up to $50 \, cm^3$, and measure the pH after each $5 \, cm^3$ addition. Wash the electrodes with distilled water between measurements.

4. Repeat the procedure for all combinations of the acids and alkalis.

5. Plot graphs of volume of alkali/cm^3 added to the acid on the *x*-axis against pH on the *y*-axis. Read off the pH at the equivalence point for each titration.

Sample results

Vol of NaOH added/ cm^3	pH	
	HCl	CH$_3$COOH
0	2.0	3.3
5	2.1	4.3
10	2.2	4.7
15	2.3	5.0
20	2.6	5.4
25	11.2	6.0
30	11.7	11.5
35	11.8	11.5
40	11.8	11.8
45	11.9	11.9
50	12.0	12.0

Vol of NH$_4$OH added/ cm^3	pH	
	HCl	CH$_3$COOH
0	2.0	3.3
5	2.2	4.4
10	2.3	4.8
15	2.4	5.0
20	2.6	5.4
25	7.0	5.8
30	8.6	7.9
35	9.0	8.9
40	9.2	9.2
45	9.3	9.2
50	9.3	9.3

Titration	pH at the equivalence point
Strong acid/strong base	7
Strong acid/weak base	5
Weak acid/strong base	9
Weak acid/weak base	no distinct equivalence point

Notes

1. The results correspond with the use of the following indicators:

   Strong acid/strong base: bromothymol blue ($pK_a = 7.0$)

   Strong acid/weak base: methyl red ($pK_a = 5.1$)

   Weak acid/strong base: phenolphthalein ($pK_a = 9.3$)

   Weak acid/weak base: no suitable indicator because the pH range of the equivalence point is too vague.

2. Indicators are weak acids. At equilibrium:

   $HA \rightleftharpoons H^+ + A^-$ where A^- is the conjugate base of the acid.

   $$K_a = \frac{[H^+] \, [A^-]}{[HA]}$$

   Taking $\log_{10}$: $\log_{10} K_a = \log_{10}[H^+] + \log_{10}\frac{[A^-]}{[HA]}$

   At the point of colour change, $[A^-] = [HA]$ so $\log_{10}\frac{[A^-]}{[HA]} = 0$

   $-\log_{10}$ is denoted as p, so $pK_a = pH$

   Therefore, the most suitable indicators for titrations are those which have pK_a values within the pH range of the equivalence point for the titration.

7 HARDNESS OF WATER

Hard water is water which will not form a lasting lather with soap. Water can be temporarily or permanently hard. Temporary hardness is caused by calcium hydrogencarbonate in the water. Carbon dioxide dissolves in rain to form carbonic acid. The carbonic acid reacts with calcium carbonate in chalky areas to form calcium hydrogencarbonate.

Temporary hardness can be removed by boiling the water. Boiling reverses the chemical reactions which made the water hard in the first place:

$$H_2O + CO_2 \rightarrow H_2CO_3$$
$$H_2CO_3 + CaCO_3 \rightarrow Ca(HCO_3)_2$$
$$Ca(HCO_3)_2 \xrightarrow{\text{boiling}} CaCO_3 + H_2O + CO_2$$

Stalagmites and stalactites in underground caves and the 'limescale' in your kettle are the result of temporary water hardness.

Permanent hardness is caused by calcium sulfate(VI) in calcareous soils which dissolves in rain as it percolates through the soil and into underground aquifers. Calcium sulfate(VI) cannot be removed by boiling. Instead, chemical methods must be used to remove the calcium or to render it inactive.

7.1 Investigating the types of substances which make water hard

Aqueous soap solution (6 g of scrapings from a bar of soap + 100 cm^3 of methylated spirit made up to 1 dm^3 with distilled water)
Calcium chloride
Sodium chloride
Magnesium chloride
Potassium chloride

Five test-tubes with bungs
Distilled water
Spatula
Teat pipette (dropper)
Measuring cylinder (10 cm^3)
Top-pan balance
Eye protection

Safety Methylated spirit is highly flammable. Anhydrous calcium chloride is irritant.

Method

1. Using the measuring cylinder, transfer 10 cm^3 of distilled water to each of the test-tubes.

2. Add 0.1 g of each of the four salts to each of four tubes and leave the other untreated as a control.

3. Close the tubes with bungs and shake them to dissolve the salts.

4. Add the soap solution, dropwise, shaking the tube after the addition of each drop until a lather which lasts for 1 minute is formed.

5. Display the results as a bar chart.

Sample results

Treatment	No. of drops
Control	6
NaCl	8
$CaCl_2$	102
KCl	9
$MgCl_2$	65

Notes

1. The hardest water is the sample which required the most soap to produce a lasting lather.

2. The results show that divalent cations produce the hardest water, calcium having the biggest effect.

3. Keep the soap solution warm throughout the experiment otherwise the soap will become too viscous to use.

4. The experiment can be extended for more able and A-level students by measuring the volume of soap solution using a burette, instead of just counting drops from a teat pipette, and also testing a greater variety of compounds, e.g., chlorides, sulfates and nitrates of group I, II and III elements of the Periodic Table, as well as carbonates of groups I and II.

7.2 Softening temporarily hard water by boiling

Limewater

Apparatus for generating carbon dioxide (see Chapter 16)

Aqueous soap solution (see Experiment 7.1.)

Teat pipette (dropper)

Distilled water

Three test-tubes

Beaker ($250 \, cm^3$)

Anti-bumping granules

Spatula

Measuring cylinder ($50 \, cm^3$)

Bunsen burner

Tripod and gauze

Safety Low hazard.

Method

1. Prepare beforehand some temporarily hard water by bubbling carbon dioxide through limewater. The initial precipitate of calcium carbonate will dissolve to produce a solution of calcium hydrogencarbonate in about 20 minutes.

2. Using the measuring cylinder, transfer 50 cm^3 of temporarily hard water to the beaker. Add some anti-bumping granules and boil for about 3 minutes.

3. Transfer 10 cm^3 of boiled and unboiled temporarily hard water and distilled water to each of three test-tubes.

4. Compare the hardness in each water sample using soap solution as described in Experiment 7.1.

Sample results

Sample	No. of drops
Distilled water	6
Unboiled temporarily hard water	96
Boiled temporarily hard water	8

Notes

1. The results show that boiling softens temporarily hard water.

2. The beaker of boiled water had a white deposit on the inside surface of the glass. This was precipitated calcium carbonate.

7.3 Determination of the ratio between temporary and permanent hardness in tap water

Beaker (250 cm^3)
Antibumping granules
Measuring cylinder (10 cm^3)
Aqueous soap solution (see Experiment 7.1.)

Teat pipette (dropper)
Bunsen burner
Tripod and gauze
Distilled water
Three test-tubes

Safety Low hazard.

Method

Carry out the procedure as described in Experiment 7.2 using distilled water and boiled and unboiled tap water.

Sample results

Sample	No. of drops
Distilled water	6
Unboiled tap water	106
Boiled tap water	39

Note

Subtracting the result for the control (distilled water) from the treated and untreated tap water results shows that 33% of the hardness remained after boiling the water. Therefore the ratio between permanent : temporary hardness = 1:2.

7.4 Chemical methods of softening hard water

Sodium carbonate
Calcium hydroxide
Sodium polytrioxophosphate(V)
    (Calgon)
Aqueous soap solution (see
    Experiment 7.1.)
Teat pipette (dropper)

Three beakers ($250\,cm^3$)
Spoon spatula
Distilled water
Five test-tubes
Measuring cylinders ($100\,cm^3$
    and $10\,cm^3$)
Glass rod

Safety Low hazard. **Solid $Ca(OH)_2$ and Na_2CO_3 are irritant.**

Method

1. Transfer $100\,cm^3$ of tap water into each of three beakers.

2. Add one rounded spatula measure of sodium carbonate to the first beaker, calcium hydroxide to the second and Calgon to the third beaker.

3. Stir with the glass rod and then test $10\,cm^3$ of water from each beaker for hardness using soap solution (see 7.1). Test the hardness of $10\,cm^3$ of untreated tap water for comparison and also distilled water as a control.

Sample results

Sample	No. of drops
Distilled water	6
Untreated tap water	91
Tap water + Na_2CO_3	8
Tap water + $Ca(OH)_2$	42
Tap water + Calgon	7

Notes

1. Sodium carbonate and Calgon softened the water completely. Sodium carbonate removed the calcium by precipitating it as calcium carbonate. The water became cloudy after the sodium carbonate had been added:

   $$Na_2CO_3 + Ca^{2+} \rightarrow CaCO_3 + 2Na^+$$

2. Calgon softened the water by 'capturing' the calcium ions and 'locking' them up so that, although they remained in solution, they were rendered inactive:

   $$2(NaPO_3)_6 + 6Ca^{2+} \rightarrow [Ca(PO_3)_2]_6 + 12Na^+$$

3. Calcium hydroxide removed only the temporary hardness from the tap water:

   $$Ca(HCO_3)_2 + Ca(OH)_2 \rightarrow 2CaCO_3 + 2H_2O$$

7.5 Softening temporarily hard water with slaked lime

Beaker ($250 \, cm^3$)
Measuring cylinders (10 and $100 \, cm^3$)
Spatula
Top-pan balance
Calcium hydroxide
Conical flask with side arm fitted with a Hirsch filter funnel and bung and pressure tubing on the side arm
Filter paper discs to fit the filter funnel
Suction pump
Distilled water

Soap solution
Teat pipette (dropper)
Bunsen burner
Tripod and gauze
Anti-bumping granules
Glass rod with a rubber policeman fitted to one end
Forceps
Temporarily hard water (see Experiment 7.2 for preparation)
Access to oven

Safety Low hazard. $Ca(OH)_2$ is irritant

Method

1. Using the measuring cylinder, transfer $100\,cm^3$ of temporarily hard water to a beaker.

2. Add a pinch of anti-bumping granules and boil for five minutes.

3. Weigh a disc of filter paper.

4. Fit the filter-paper disc to the Hirsch funnel assembly connected to the suction pump and quantitatively transfer the precipitated calcium carbonate to the filter funnel. Use the rubber policeman to remove the precipitated calcium carbonate from the internal surface of the beaker and the anti-bumping granules. Take care not to transfer any anti-bumping granules.

5. Filter off the precipitated calcium carbonate and wash three times with distilled water.

6. Using forceps, remove the filter paper disc from the funnel and dry to constant weight in an oven set at $100\,°C$ or on a gauze over a light bulb.

7. Weigh the filter paper and calcium carbonate and find the mass of calcium carbonate by subtraction.

8. Calculate the mass of calcium hydroxide required to precipitate this mass of calcium carbonate from $100\,cm^3$ of temporarily hard water from:

   $Ca(OH)_2 + Ca(HCO_3)_2 \rightarrow 2CaCO_3 + 2H_2O$

   i.e. $74 \div 200 \times$ mass of $CaCO_3$ precipitated.

9. Add this amount of calcium hydroxide to a fresh $100\,cm^3$ of temporarily hard water, stir well with a glass rod, filter and test $10\,cm^3$ of the filtrate for hardness using soap solution.

10. Test $10\,cm^3$ of the original untreated temporarily hard water before and after boiling for hardness and compare the results.

Sample results

Mass of filter paper = 0.03 g

Mass of filter paper + residue = 0.12 g

Mass of residue = 0.09 g

Mass of $Ca(OH)_2$ to add = 0.03 g

Tests for water hardness

Sample	Vol/cm^3 of soap solution required to produce a lather
Untreated	6.1
Boiled	1.8
Ca(OH)$_2$	2.1

Notes

1. Temporary hardness in water is caused by calcium hydrogencarbonate which is formed by carbonic acid in rain water reacting with calcium carbonate in chalky areas.

$$H_2CO_3 + CaCO_3 \rightarrow Ca(HCO_3)_2$$

2. Boiling removes temporary hardness from water by precipitating calcium carbonate:

$$Ca(HCO_3)_2 \rightarrow CaCO_3 + CO_2 + H_2O$$

3. The results show that calcium hydroxide removes the temporary hardness from the water.

7.6 The use of ion exchange resins to soften hard water

Permutit cationic exchange resin
Burette (50 cm^3)
Copper(II) sulfate(VI) solution (1 mol dm^{-3})

Sulfuric(VI) acid (1 mol dm^{-3})
Two retort stands and clamps
Four beakers (100 cm^3)

Safety 1 mol dm^{-3} copper(II) sulfate(VI) solution is harmful. 1 mol dm^{-3} sulfuric(VI) acid is irritant. The ion exchange resin should be soaked in water in a beaker before filling the burette because the beads tend to expand when absorbing water and can shatter the burette.

Method

1. Fill the burette with the previously soaked cationic exchange resin beads.

2. Hold the burette in the clamp and stand and place an empty beaker under the burette.

3. Pour copper(II) sulfate(VI) solution through the resin column.

4. Note the colour of the leachate in the beaker.

5. Replace the beaker under the burette with a new one and pour sulfuric(VI) acid through the resin column.

6. Note the colour of the leachate in the beakers.

Results

The leachate from the resin column treated with copper(II) sulfate(VI) was colourless. The sulfuric(VI) acid leachate was blue.

Note

The resin removed the copper ions from the solution by exchanging them for hydrogen ions which were held on the resin. Sulfuric(VI) acid recharged the resin by putting hydrogen ions back on the resin and eluting the copper ions. Domestic water softeners contain a special type of clay which contains exchangeable sodium ions. The calcium ions in hard water change places with sodium ions on the clay. In this way the clay softens the water by removing the calcium. When all of the exchange sites are occupied by calcium, the clay has to be recharged by washing it with a solution of sodium chloride so that the sodium ions are put back onto the clay in order that it can be used again.

7.7 Softening water by distillation

For apparatus/reagents see Chapter 1 Figure 1.6.

Safety Use anti-bumping granules to prevent bumping when the water in the flask boils.

Method

1. Fill the distillation flask with tap water.

2. Collect the distillate and test the distillate and original tap water for hardness using soap solution (see Experiment 7.1).

Sample results

Sample	No. of drops
Tap water	117
Distillate	6

Note

The dissolved salts which make water hard are not volatile and so they remain in the distillation flask so that only pure water is collected from the Liebig condenser.

7.8 Comparing the purity of water from different sources

Four beakers (100 cm³)
Measuring cylinder (50 cm³)
Bunsen burner
Tripod and gauze
Top-pan balance
Anti-bumping granules
Bottled drinking water (Perrier or Evian)

Samples of sea water prepared by dissolving 25 g of sodium chloride in 1 dm³ of distilled water
Rain water
Tongs
Heatproof mat
Eye protection

Safety **Avoid the use of carbonated water which may fizz or froth. Beware of spitting when evaporating to dryness. Take care to avoid scalds and burns from the boiling water and hot apparatus.**

Method

1. Add a pinch of anti-bumping granules to a 100 cm³ beaker and weigh it.

2. Using a measuring cylinder, transfer 50 cm³ of water to the beaker.

3. Put the beaker on a tripod and gauze over a Bunsen burner and boil until completely dry.

4. Using tongs, remove the beaker to a heatproof mat.

5. When cool weigh the beaker and residue.

6. Repeat the procedure for each sample of water.

Results

Sample	Beaker empty/g	Beaker + residue/g	Residue/g
Sea water	50.84	52.34	1.50
Rain water	48.42	48.56	0.01
Perrier	48.62	48.63	0.01
Tap water	49.84	50.21	0.37

Notes

1. The water with the least mass of residue is the purest.

2. The anti-bumping granules provide gentle boiling.

3. This is a useful activity at KS3 for students to practise gravimetric techniques together with logical deduction.

8 BONDING

A chemical bond is an electrostatic force of attraction holding together two atomic nuclei and a pair of electrons. If the nuclei have equal forces of attraction for the bonding electrons then the electrons are shared equally between the nuclei, and the bond is covalent. In a covalent bond, each atom contributes one electron to make up the bond pair. If both electrons are provided by only one atom then the bond is a dative covalent bond or a co-ordinate bond. If one of the nuclei exerts a greater force of attraction than the other for the bonding electrons then unequal sharing of the electrons takes place and the bond becomes polarised. If the degree of polarisation is such that one nucleus takes complete control of the bonding electrons, then electron transfer from one atom to the other takes place and the bond is ionic. Covalent and ionic bonds are extreme cases. Most bonds are intermediate in character between these two extremes. Evidence for ionic bonding in a compound is the electrical conductivity of the compound when molten or dissolved in water. The ions must be free to move for an ionic compound to conduct electricity.

8.1 Testing a variety of liquids for the presence of ions

Two graphite rods
Two crocodile clips
Three connecting leads with 4 mm plugs at each end. Ammeter (0–5 A)
Distilled water
Absorbent paper tissues
6 V dc power supply
Eye protection

A variety of solutions of salts (1 mol dm^{-3}) and a variety of organic liquids in beakers (100 cm^3), e.g. solutions of: sodium chloride, copper(II) sulfate(VI), calcium chloride, ammonium nitrate(V), potassium nitrate(V), magnesium sulfate(VI), sucrose; tap water, cyclohexane, ethanol, propanone, liquid paraffin, cooking oil, distilled water

Safety **Ammonium nitrate(V) and potassium nitrate(V) are oxidising agents and cause fire with combustible materials. Copper(II) sulfate(VI) is harmful. Cyclohexane, ethanol and propanone are highly flammable. Cyclohexane and propanone dissolve the natural oils in skin so avoid skin contact. Calcium chloride is irritant.**

Method

1. By means of the crocodile clips and connecting leads, connect the two graphite rods in series with the ammeter and power supply.

2. Immerse the graphite rods in each liquid in turn and note the ammeter reading. Once you have noted the current, switch off as some of the solutions produce hazardous gases.

3. Wash the graphite rods in a beaker of distilled water and blot dry with absorbent paper tissue between each test.

4. Liquids which conduct contain compounds that are ionically bonded and liquids that do not conduct are covalently bonded.

Results

Ionic: Aqueous solutions of: sodium chloride, copper(II) sulfate(VI), calcium chloride, ammonium nitrate(V), potassium nitrate(V), magnesium sulfate(VI), tap water.

Covalent: Aqueous sucrose solution, cyclohexane, ethanol, propanone, liquid paraffin, cooking oil, distilled water.

Note

Electrolytes are molten salts or aqueous solutions of salts which contain ions. The ions carry the current through conducting liquids. Liquids which do not contain ions do not conduct electricity.

8.2 Electrolysis of molten lead(II) bromide

Bunsen burner
Tripod and gauze
Retort stand and clamp
12 V dc power supply
Three connecting leads with 4 mm plugs at each end
Two crocodile clips

Two graphite rods set in a rubber bung
Evaporating basin
Spatula
Lead(II) bromide
Eye protection
Access to a fume cupboard

Safety Lead(II) bromide is toxic. The effects are cumulative. Pregnant women or younger pupils should not handle this substance. There is the danger of damage to the unborn child. The experiment must be done in a fume cupboard because the bromine vapour produced during the electrolysis is very toxic and corrosive.

Method

1. Assemble the apparatus as shown in Figure 8.1.

2. Switch on the power supply and heat the lead(II) bromide using the Bunsen burner.

3. Observe the lamp as the lead(II) bromide melts.

4. When the lead bromide has melted fully, remove the Bunsen burner and allow the molten lead(II) bromide to cool.

5. Observe the lamp as the molten lead(II) bromide solidifies.

6. Dismantle the apparatus and inspect the solid lead(II) bromide under each electrode.

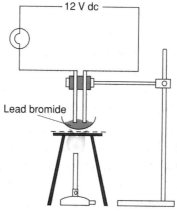

Figure 8.1 Electrolysis of molten lead(II) bromide.

Sample results

Whilst the lead(II) bromide remained solid the lamp did not light. When the lead(II) bromide began to melt the lamp glowed dimly and became fully bright when all of the lead(II) bromide had melted. As the lead(II) bromide began to solidify the lamp became dim and ceased to glow when all of the lead(II) bromide had solidified. A globule of lead was detected under the cathode and the brown colour of bromine appeared under the anode.

Notes

1. The results showed that current only flowed (as indicated by the glowing lamp) when the ions were free to move, i.e. when the lead(II) bromide had melted to a liquid.

2. The equations for the electrolysis:

At the cathode: $Pb^{2+} + 2e^- \rightarrow Pb$

At the anode: $2Br^- - 2e^- \rightarrow Br_2$

8.3 Electrical conductivity of molten glass

Bunsen burner

Two retort stands with clamps

50 cm of glass rod (6 mm cross section diameter) with rubber bungs at each end

Electric fire

Mains lamp (carbon filament)

Safety screen

Two pieces of copper wire (1 mm cross section diameter) each sleeved with insulation material but with 20 cm of bare wire exposed at one end for winding round the glass rod. These wires to be connected to the terminal block of a connector box (see Figure 8.2).

Safety The wires from the glass rod should be sleeved with insulation material and connected to the mains through a specially constructed connector box containing a 6 A standard screw terminal block and 13 A square pin sockets (Figure 8.2). Do not use 4 mm plugs and crocodile clips. An electric fire should be connected in series with the apparatus to act as a ballast. Switch off the mains using the mains residual current circuit breaker before assembling the apparatus. Ensure that the Bunsen burner and the retort stands are connected to Earth via the connecting box. Connections to the Bunsen burner and retort stands are best made by unscrewing the bases and winding the wire at the base of the thread and then re-assembling. Check that the connections are firm. Switch off the mains at the mains residual current circuit breaker before dismantling the apparatus. Perform the experiment behind a safety screen so that the students cannot touch the apparatus.

The connecting box

This is made from a double 13 A square pin electrical socket and a five-section length cut from a standard 6 A terminal block mounted onto a board made of $24 \times 18 \times 0.5$ cm ply wood. The socket and terminal block are wired as shown in Figure 8.2. The board and the wired components are covered by a polythene ice-cream tub $22 \times 16 \times 8$ cm which has arches cut in the sides for the connecting wires. The cover is held in place with Gaffa tape.

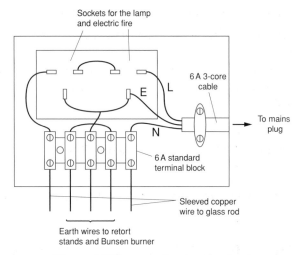

Figure 8.2 Diagram of connecting box.

Method

1. Clean the bare copper wires with emery cloth and wrap them in a spiral around the glass rod. Leave a 2 cm gap between the ends of the spirals where they meet (see Figure 8.3).

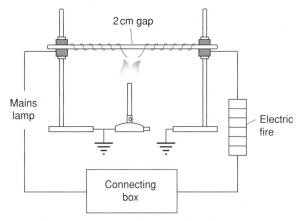

Figure 8.3 Electrical conductivity of molten glass.

2. Ensure good contact between the glass rod and the copper wire spirals.

3. Put a safety screen between the apparatus and the audience.

4. Light the Bunsen burner, then put the plug in the mains socket and switch on. Then switch on the mains residual current circuit breaker switch.

5. Observe the lamp as the glass rod begins to soften.

6. Switch off at the mains residual current circuit breaker as soon as the effect is observed.

7. Switch off at the mains plug and remove the mains plug from the socket before dismantling the apparatus as an added safety precaution.

Results

The lamp showed that molten glass conducted electricity at high voltage.

Note

Ions are free to move in molten glass, which allows it to conduct electricity.

8.4 Temperature changes during formation and boiling points of liquid mixtures of different composition

Twin necked pear-shaped flask set up
    for reflux
Liebig condenser
Thermometer
Boiling tubes in a rack
Six burettes ($50\,cm^3$)
Ethanol
Cyclohexane

Ethyl ethanoate
Propan-1-ol
Propan-2-ol
Trichloromethane
Beaker ($100\,cm^3$)
Cotton wool
Eye protection

Safety Trichloromethane is a skin irritant and a category 3 carcinogen. Experiments using mixtures containing these reagents should be done in a fume cupboard. Cyclohexane, ethyl ethanoate and the alcohols are all harmful and highly flammable.

Method

1. Put each liquid into a burette.

2. Place a boiling tube in the beaker and surround the tube with cotton wool. Keep a second boiling tube available in a boiling-tube rack.

3. Run $18\,cm^3$ of one liquid into the insulated boiling-tube and $2\,cm^3$ of the second liquid into the other boiling tube.

4. Measure the temperature of each liquid.

5. Tip the liquid in the free tube into the insulated tube, stir the mixture with the thermometer and find the temperature change.

6. Repeat the procedure for the following mixtures:

Liquid A/cm³:	20	18	15	12	8	5	2	0
Liquid B/cm³:	0	2	5	8	12	15	18	20

where A and B are trichloromethane and ethyl ethanoate,
cyclohexane and ethanol, and propan-1-ol and propan-2-ol.

5. Transfer each mixture in turn to the flask of the reflux apparatus and
    measure the boiling point.

6. Plot line graphs of temperature changes against mixture
    composition and boiling temperature against mixture composition.

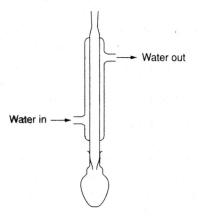

Figure 8.4 Reflux.

Results

Percentage composition		A: CHCl₃ B: CH₃COOCH₃		A: C₆H₁₂ B: C₂H₅OH		A: CH₃(CH₂)₂OH B: CH₃CH(OH)CH₃	
A	**B**	**T/°C**	**b.p./°C**	**T/°C**	**b.p./°C**	**T/°C**	**b.p./°C**
100	0	20	33	20	82	20	97
90	10	25	64	15	76	20	95
75	25	30	73	12	72	20	93
60	40	31	76	10	70	20	91
40	60	30	80	8	71	20	88
25	75	27	81	10	73	20	86
10	90	24	83	12	76	20	84
0	100	20	83	20	78	20	81

Notes

1. Energy changes produce changes in temperature. The temperature changes indicate changes taking place in the intermolecular bonding of the components of the mixture. Intermolecular bonds are of three main types: van der Waals forces of attraction, permanent dipole-dipole attractions and hydrogen bonding which is a specific type of dipole-dipole attraction. Cyclohexane is van der Waals bonded. Ethanol is hydrogen bonded. When these liquids are mixed the temperature drops because the cyclohexane particles disrupt the hydrogen bonding between particles of ethanol. Breaking bonds is endothermic and requires an input of energy. Trichloromethane and ethyl ethanoate are both polar. When these liquids are mixed, stronger dipole-dipole attractions occur between the particles of these liquids than were already in place and the temperature increases. Bond forming is an exothermic process. Propan-1-ol and propan-2-ol are both hydrogen bonded to the same extent and so there is no temperature change when these liquids are mixed.

2. A linear relationship between the percentage composition of the mixture and its boiling point means that there are equal forces of attraction between all particles. A non-linear relationship means that the forces of attraction between particles of the same species is different from the forces of attraction between particles of different species. Mixtures whose boiling points deviate positively from linearity have stronger intermolecular bonding between particles of different species than with particles of the same species, so that the particles of the higher boiling point liquid hold back the particles of the lower boiling point liquid, thereby diminishing their escaping tendency when the mixture boils. Conversely, mixtures which deviate negatively have weaker intermolecular bonds between particles of different species and this enhances the escaping tendency of the particles.

9 ENERGY CHANGES

The study of energy change involves the system and its surroundings. The particles of the reactants/products mixture make up the system. The surroundings comprise the solvent, the container and the air (unless these actively take part in the reaction to become part of the system).

The most common energy change is a heat change (enthalpy change) which causes a temperature change in the surroundings. We use a thermometer to measure changes in temperature and so the thermometer is part of the surroundings.

Changes in which energy is transferred from the surroundings to the reacting system cause a decrease in the temperature of the surroundings and such a change is endothermic. Energy flowing from the system to the surroundings raises the temperature of the surroundings and the change is exothermic.

Physical changes involve changes of state, e.g. melting, boiling, sublimation, etc. Melting is an endothermic process because the particles speed up during the transition from solid to liquid and so need the kinetic energy to do so. This energy is absorbed from the surroundings and so the surroundings become colder. Conversely, the surroundings get hotter when a liquid freezes because the particles lose kinetic energy in slowing down. This is why solids melt when we heat them because we are providing the particles with kinetic energy to speed up. The energy required to turn 1 kg of solid into 1 kg of liquid is called the latent heat of fusion. Turning a liquid into a gas also requires an input of energy because the particles of a gas have more kinetic energy than the particles of a liquid. When we boil liquids we are providing the particles with the kinetic energy to make the transition. The energy required to turn 1 kg of liquid into 1 kg of gas is called the latent heat of vaporisation. Condensation is an exothermic process because the particles transfer their kinetic energy to the surroundings in order to slow down as the gas liquefies so the surroundings get hotter.

During a chemical change existing bonds in the reactants break and new bonds form to make the products. Bond breaking requires energy – an endothermic process. Bond forming releases energy – an exothermic process. If the temperature of the surroundings falls then more energy is taken in to break existing bonds than is released in forming new ones so the overall energy change is endothermic. If, on the other hand, more energy is released in forming new bonds than is absorbed in breaking existing ones, the overall energy change is exothermic and the surroundings get hotter.

9.1 Dissolving substances in water

Spoon spatula
Thermometer
Eight expanded polystyrene drinks cups
Ammonium nitrate(V)
Ammonium chloride
Potassium nitrate(V)
Calcium oxide
Anhydrous copper(II) sulfate(VI)
Sodium carbonate-citric acid mixture
   (1:1)

Concentrated sulfuric(VI) acid
Calcium sulfate(VI) hemihydrate
   (Plaster of Paris)
Measuring cylinders (10 cm^3 and
   25 cm^3)
Distilled water
Eye protection

Safety **Concentrated sulfuric(VI) acid is corrosive. Potassium nitrate(V) and ammonium nitrate(V) are both oxidising agents and cause fire with combustible materials. Copper(II) sulfate(VI) and ammonium chloride are harmful. Calcium oxide is an irritant.**

Method

1. Using the measuring cylinder, transfer 25 cm^3 of distilled water to each of the cups.

2. Measure the temperature of the water in the cups.

3. Wearing eye protection, carefully add 1 cm^3 of sulfuric(VI) acid to one cup of distilled water and stir with the thermometer.

4. Add Plaster of Paris to the water in another cup sufficient to produce a creamy texture. Put a thermometer in the mixture.

5. Add one rounded spatula measure of each of the substances to each of the other cups of water and stir with the thermometer.

6. Measure the temperature again when the temperature change is maximum.

Sample results

Substance	Temp. change/°C	Inference
NH_4Cl	−4	endothermic
NH_4NO_3	−5	endothermic
KNO_3	−8	endothermic
$CuSO_4$	+6	exothermic
Na_2CO_3 + citric acid	−4	endothermic
Conc. H_2SO_4	+11	exothermic
Plaster of Paris	+10	exothermic

Notes

1. When ammonium chloride, ammonium nitrate(V) and potassium nitrate(V) dissolve in water the crystal lattices of these salts break up and the ions dissociate. Once dissociated, the ions hydrate to form the aqueous solutions. The energy absorbed in breaking the lattices (lattice energy) is greater than the energy released when the ions hydrate (hydration energy) and so the overall process is endothermic.

2. Calcium oxide reacts chemically with water to form calcium hydroxide:

    $$CaO + H_2O \rightarrow Ca(OH)_2$$

    The bonds forming calcium hydroxide contain less energy than the bonds forming water and calcium oxide so the overall reaction is exothermic.

3. Adding anhydrous copper(II) sulfate(VI) to water dissociates the ions, which is an endothermic process, and produces $[Cu(H_2O)_4]^{2+}$ ions which is an exothermic process. The energy released in forming the copper-water bonds in the complex ion exceeds the lattice energy and so the overall process is exothermic.

4. Adding sodium carbonate/citric acid mixture to water is endothermic because the increase in kinetic energy of the escaping carbon dioxide is much greater than the energy released in forming the products of the reaction.

5. The reaction between concentrated sulfuric(VI) acid and water is exothermic because the energy released when the ions hydrate exceeds the energy required to dissociate the ions.

6. When Plaster of Paris sets, the reaction is exothermic due to hydration forming extra bonds with the added water to form gypsum:

    $$(CaSO_4)_2.H_2O + 3H_2O \rightarrow 2CaSO_4.2H_2O$$

    Also the particles need to lose some of their kinetic energy when the material solidifies.

9.2 Changes of state

Ethoxyethane (ether)
Source of compressed air, e.g.
   bellows, aquarium pumps
Super-saturated aqueous sodium
   thiosulfate (Hypo) solution in a
   small test tube (5×50 mm)
One crystal of sodium thiosulfate
Barium hydroxide ($Ba(OH)_2.8H_2O$)
Ammonium chloride
Scrap paper

Spatula
Thermometer
Beaker (100 cm^3)
Glass rod
Top-pan balance
Watch glass
Eye protection
Access to an open window with an
   outside window ledge or fume
   cupboard

Safety Ethoxyethane is an anaesthetic and extremely flammable so the experiment in which this is used must be done by an open window or in a fume cupboard. There must not be any naked flames in the room because long distance flashbacks can occur. Barium hydroxide and ammonium chloride are harmful. Add dilute sulfuric(VI) acid prior to disposal. This converts the barium compounds to insoluble barium sulfate(VI) which is safe to handle.

Method

1. Half fill a 100 cm^3 beaker with ether. Add a little water to the watch glass and stand the beaker of ether in the watch glass containing the water. Place the whole thing on the outside window ledge or in a fume cupboard and completely evaporate the ether using compressed air.

2. Carefully immerse the thermometer in the super-saturated Hypo solution and note its temperature. Then add the crystal of Hypo and note the temperature change as the solution freezes.

3. Weigh out 32 g of barium hydroxide into a 100 cm^3 beaker. Weigh out 10 g of ammonium chloride on a piece of scrap paper. Place the beaker of barium hydroxide in a little water in a watch glass. Add the ammonium chloride while stirring using a glass rod.

Sample results

1. The evaporation of ether freezes the beaker to the watch glass.

2. There is a rise in temperature of about $60°C$ as the Hypo solution freezes.

3. The barium hydroxide-ammonium chloride mixture melts and this is accompanied by the beaker becoming frozen to the watch glass.

Notes

1. All of the temperature changes are associated with changes of state and can be explained using kinetic theory.

2. The reaction which takes place when barium hydroxide and ammonium chloride are mixed can be represented as follows:

$$Ba(OH)_2 + 2NH_4Cl \rightarrow 2NH_3 + BaCl_2 + 2H_2O$$

The barium chloride dissolves in the water both of which are produced by the reaction, and the ammonia is released as a gas. The dissociation of barium and chloride ions together with the production of the gas are both endothermic processes which contribute to the drop in temperature caused by the change of state of the mixture.

9.3 'Fireworks'

These reactions are very violent and should only be carried out by an experienced chemist. All the demonstrations must be carried out behind safety screens.

Safety Protect the bench by covering it with heatproof mats before carrying out these reactions. Have a sand bucket ready to quench any of the reactions should they get out of hand. If a reaction mixture fails to react then approach it with caution and cover it with sand before disposal. Wear a face shield when carrying out these demonstrations. The students should wear eye protection.

9.3.1 Reaction between magnesium powder and copper(II) oxide

Copper(II) oxide
Magnesium powder
Magnesium ribbon
Spatulas
Jam-jar lid
Top-pan balance

Bunsen burner
Tripod and gauze
Scrap paper
Heatproof mat
Safety screens
Eye protection and face shield

Safety Copper(II) oxide is harmful. Magnesium ribbon and powder are both highly flammable. The paint of the jam-jar lids may burn and produce unpleasant odours.

Method

1. Mix 16 g of copper oxide with 5 g of magnesium powder and transfer the mixture to a jam-jar lid. Using a spatula, scoop the mixture into a heap and put a fuse consisting of 15 cm of magnesium ribbon in the mixture as shown in Figure 9.1.

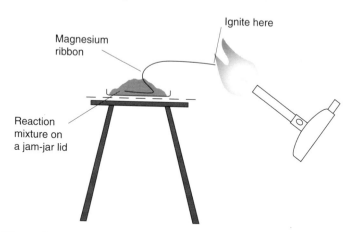

Figure 9.1 Igniting an incendiary mixture using a magnesium fuse.

2. Put the lid with its contents on a tripod and gauze. With the safety screen in place light the fuse using a Bunsen burner and retreat to a safe distance.

Note

Equation for the reaction:

$$Mg + CuO \rightarrow MgO + Cu$$

9.3.2 Reaction between zinc powder and sulfur

Zinc powder

Flowers of sulfur

Magnesium ribbon

Spatulas

Jam-jar lid

Top-pan balance

Bunsen burner

Tripod and gauze

Scrap paper

Heatproof mat

Safety screens

Access to fume cupboard

Safety Zinc powder is flammable. Sulfur burns to produce a corrosive and toxic gas which can trigger an asthma attack in susceptible people.

Method

1. To check that zinc powder is not oxidised beyond use, do a trial run before the lesson in a fume cupboard.

2. Repeat the procedure given in 9.3.1 using a mixture of 5 g of zinc powder and 2.5 g of flowers of sulfur.

Note

Equation for the reaction:

$$Zn + S \rightarrow ZnS$$

9.3.3 The Thermit reaction

Aluminium powder
Iron(III) oxide
Barium peroxide
Spatulas
Jam-jar lid
Top-pan balance

Bunsen burner
Tripod and gauze
Scrap paper
Heatproof mat
Safety screens
Access to fume cupboard

Safety Aluminium powder is highly flammable. Barium peroxide is an oxidising agent and harmful. This reaction produces flying molten iron so the demonstration should be done in a fume cupboard, behind safety screens. Close the front of the fume cupboard soon after igniting the fuse in order to contain any flying molten iron.

Method

Repeat the procedure given in 9.3.1 using a mixture of 5.4 g of aluminium powder and 16 g of iron(III) oxide. Put a little barium peroxide in a well around the magnesium fuse at the top of the mixture before igniting the fuse.

Note

Equation for the reaction:

$$2Al + Fe_2O_3 \rightarrow Al_2O_3 + 2Fe$$

9.3.4 Reaction between potassium manganate(VII) and glycerol

Potassium manganate(VII)	Teat pipette
Glycerol	Beaker of water
Spatula	Scrap paper
Jam-jar lid	Heatproof mat
Top-pan balance	Safety screens
Tripod and gauze	

Safety Potassium manganate(VII) is an oxidising agent and harmful.

Method

1. Put 20 g of potassium manganate(VII) in a heap on a jam-jar lid.

2. Make a well in the top of the heap and add one drop of water from a dropper.

3. Put the lid with its contents onto a tripod and gauze and fill the well with glycerol.

4. Observe the reaction from a safe distance.

Note

Equation for the reaction:

$$2KMnO_4 + CH_2(OH)CH(OH)CH_2(OH) \rightarrow 2MnO_2 + K_2CO_3 + 4H_2O + 3C$$

9.3.5 Reaction between magnesium and potassium nitrate(V)

Magnesium powder	Two connecting wires with 4 mm plugs
Potassium nitrate(V)	at each end
Spatula	Two crocodile clips
Top-pan balance	26 swg constantan wire
Scrap paper	Heatproof mat
12 V dc power supply	Safety screens

Safety Magnesium powder is highly flammable. Potassium nitrate(V) is an oxidising agent and will cause fire with combustible materials. This reaction is not covered by any of the commonly used model (general) risk assessments. A special risk assessment would be required.

Method

1. Hold a piece of constantan wire onto a heatproof mat using crocodile clips.

2. Prepare a 1:1 mixture of magnesium powder and potassium nitrate(V).

3. Pour the mixture in a heap over the constantain wire.

4. Connect the two crocodile clips to the 12 V supply and switch on the power to ignite the mixture.

Notes

1. Substitute strontium nitrate(V) for potassium nitrate(V) to produce a red flash. A green flash can be produced from a mixture containing equal quantities by mass of magnesium powder, boric acid, potassium nitrate(V) and flowers of sulfur. Beware of the hazards associated with oxides of sulfur produced in the reaction.

2. Equation for the reaction:

$$Mg + 2KNO_3 \rightarrow MgO + 2NO_2 + K_2O$$

9.3.6 Reaction between aluminium and iodine

Aluminium powder
Iodine
Spatulas
Jam-jar lid
Top-pan balance
Mortar and pestle

Teat pipette
Beaker of water
Heatproof mat
Safety screen
Access to a fume cupboard

Safety Iodine is harmful by skin contact and inhalation. The demonstration must be carried out in a fume cupboard.

Method

1. Grind some iodine to a fine powder using a mortar and pestle.

2. Put a mixture of equal quantities of powdered iodine and aluminium powder onto a jam-jar lid on a tripod and gauze.

3. Make a well in the top of the mixture heap and add one drop of water from a dropper. A trace of detergent in the water helps.

4. Observe the reaction from a safe distance.

Note

Equation for the reaction:

$$Al + 3I_2 \rightarrow 2AlI_3$$

9.4 Energy transfer

Expanded polystyrene drinks cup

Kettle

Thermometer

Measuring cylinder ($25\,cm^3$)

Safety Low hazard.

Method

1. Using the measuring cylinder, transfer $20\,cm^3$ of cold water to the cup and measure its temperature.

2. Heat some water in the kettle, and measure out $20\,cm^3$ in the measuring cylinder.

3. Measure the temperature of the hot water and then immediately pour it into the cold water in the cup.

4. Stir the water in the cup with the thermometer and then measure its temperature.

Sample results

Temperature of cold water = 15 °C

Temperature of hot water = 40 °C

Temperature of the mixture = 28 °C

Calculations

E = mass $\times c \times$ temperature change, where c = specific heat capacity

When mixed, heat gained by cold water = $0.02 \times 4.2 \times (28 - 15) = 1.09\,kJ$

heat lost by hot water = $0.02 \times 4.2 \times (40 - 28) = 1.01\,kJ$

Note

The results show that energy is conserved, i.e. heat lost by hot water = heat gained by cold water. This is consistent with the First Law of Thermodynamics (the Law of Conservation of Energy).

9.5 Determination of the enthalpy of reaction for the displacement of copper in copper(II) sulfate(VI) by magnesium

Expanded polystyrene drinks cup
Thermometer
Copper(II) sulfate(VI) solution
   (0.25 mol dm^{-3})
Magnesium powder
Spatula

Measuring cylinder (100 cm^3)
Top-pan balance
Scrap paper
Stop watch
Eye protection

Safety Magnesium powder is highly flammable.

Method

1. Using the measuring cylinder, transfer 100 cm^3 of copper(II) sulfate(VI) solution to the cup.

2. Weigh out 0.6 g of magnesium powder onto a piece of scrap paper.

3. Start the stop watch and begin measuring the temperature of the copper(II) sulfate(VI) at one minute intervals.

4. Between the third and fourth minute, add the magnesium powder, stir with the thermometer and continue to measure the temperature every minute until there is no further temperature change.

5. Plot a line graph of time/minute on the x-axis and temperature/°C on the y-axis.

6. Extrapolate the part of the curve from the point of maximum temperature to the point when the magnesium was added and read off the temperature change.

Results

Time/min	Temp/°C	Time/min	Temp/°C
1	18	7	33
2	18	8	34
3	18	9	35
4	22	10	35
5	25	11	35
6	32	12	35

Calculations

Equation for the reaction:

$Mg(s) + CuSO_4(aq) \rightarrow MgSO_4(aq) + Cu(s)$

Temperature change = $17\,°C$

Density of $0.25\,mol\,dm^{-3}\ CuSO_4 = 1.061\,g\,cm^{-3}$

Mass of $100\,cm^3$ of $0.25\,mol\,dm^{-3}\ CuSO_4 = 106.1\,g$

Heat change = $[(106.1 + 0.6) \div 1000] \times 4.2 \times 17 = -7.61\,kJ/0.25\,mole$

Enthalpy change = $-7.61 \div 0.25 = -30.47\,kJ/mole$

Notes

1. Enthalpy change is negative because the reaction is exothermic.
2. Heat absorbed by the cup is negligible and can be discounted.

9.6 Enthalpy change for combustion and its relationship to the C–H bond energy

Copper calorimeter with lid and stirrer
Thermometer
Measuring cylinder ($100\,cm^3$)
Clamp and stand
Kettle
Expanded polystyrene drinks cup

Spirit burners containing a range of
   different alcohols clearly labelled
Matches
Cotton wool
Top-pan balance
Four heatproof mats
Eye protection

Safety Do not take stock bottles of the alcohols into the laboratory. Use burners with a squat base. Fill burners with cotton wool in order to minimise problems of spillage or breakage.

Method

Determine the heat capacity of the calorimeter as follows:

1. Add $50\,cm^3$ of cold water to the copper can and record its temperature.

2. Add $50\,cm^3$ of hot water from the kettle to the polystyrene cup and measure its temperature.

3. Add the hot water from the cup to the cold water in the copper can and measure the temperature of the mixture.

4. Calculate the heat capacity of the calorimeter by applying the First Law of Thermodynamics:

Heat lost by = heat gained by + heat gained by
hot water   cold water   calorimeter

Determine enthalpy change for combustion as follows:

1. Put 100 cm^3 of cold water into the calorimeter held in a clamp and stand, and measure the temperature of the water.

2. Weigh a spirit burner containing an alcohol.

3. Place the burner under the base of the calorimeter and adjust the position of the clamp so that the base of the calorimeter is 2 cm above the wick of the burner. Place four heatproof mats around the apparatus to help minimise heat loss.

4. Light the wick of the burner and heat the water in the calorimeter until the temperature rises by 50 °C.

5. Extinguish the flame and reweigh the burner.

6. Calculate the mass of fuel consumed.

7. Convert mass of fuel to moles and calculate the enthalpy of combustion for the fuel from:

$\Delta H_c = (0.1 \times 4.2 \times -50 \div$ moles of fuel used)
    $+ (-$ heat capacity of the calorimeter)

because it is absorbing heat from the reaction.

8. Repeat the procedure for a range of different alcohols.

Find the energy for the C–H bond as follows:

1. Plot a line graph of the number of carbon atoms in the molecule of each alcohol on the x-axis and the enthalpy of combustion/kJ per mole on the y-axis.

2. Construct the line of best fit and find its gradient. This gives the contribution which a CH_2 group makes to the enthalpy of combustion of an alcohol.

3. The gradient ÷ 2 gives the C–H bond energy contribution to the enthalpy of combustion.

Sample results

Determination of the heat capacity of the calorimeter:

Temperature of the cold water = 15 °C

Temperature of the hot water = 40 °C

Temperature of the mixture = 26 °C

Determination of the enthalpy of combustion for alcohols:

Alcohol	Mass of fuel used/g
Methanol	1.34
Ethanol	0.64
Propan-1-ol	0.66
Butan-1-ol	0.55
Pentan-1-ol	0.57

Calculations

Heat capacity for calorimeter

$= [0.05 \times 4.2 \times (40\text{-}26)] - [0.05 \times 4.2 \times (26 - 15)]$

$= 2.94 - 2.31 = 0.43\,kJ$

Mass of methanol consumed = 1.34 g

Molar mass of methanol = 32

Moles of methanol consumed = $1.34 \div 32 = 0.042$

Enthalpy of combustion for methanol

$= (0.1 \times 4.2 \times -50 \div 0.042) + (-0.43) = -500.43\,kJ/mol.$

Enthalpies of combustion for the other alcohols/kJ per mole

Ethanol = −1477

Propan-1-ol = −1910

Butan-1-ol = −2826

Pentan-1-ol = −3243

Calculation of C–H bond energy:

Gradient of graph = CH_2 group's contribution to ΔH_c = 652 kJ/mol

C–H bond contribution = $652 \div 2 = 326\,kJ/mol$

Notes

1. Bond energy is the energy released when a covalent bond is formed between two atoms. The process is exothermic so the value should be preceded by a negative sign. The energy required to break a covalent bond is called the bond dissociation energy. It is an endothermic process and therefore has a positive value.

2. During combustion C–H, C–C and O=O bonds break and C=O and O–H bonds form:

   C–C + C–H + O=O → C=O + O–H

3. There are problems in getting good results with this experiment. This is mainly due to the difficulty in minimising heat losses during the heating of the calorimeter. The procedure as outlined would be an ideal exercise at A-level because it gives the student the opportunity to evaluate experimental plans in the light of experience gained from carrying out the task, a skill for which many students seem to have difficulty in getting high marks.

4. The graph of calculated enthalpies of combustion against number of carbon atoms in the alcohols does not intercept the origin because of the contribution of other bonds. If the line of best fit in the experimental data does not intercept the origin of the graph, then the equation:

   $y = mx + c$

   needs to be used. The gradient 'm' should then be halved and the constant 'c' added to give the C–H bond energy.

5. The published value for the average C–H bond dissociation energy is 412 kJ/mol.

9.7 Verification of Hess's Law

Sodium hydroxide pellets
Hydrochloric acid (4 mol dm^{-3})
Distilled water
Expanded polystyrene drinks cup
Thermometer

Measuring cylinder (25 cm^3)
Top-pan balance
Watch glass
Spatula
Safety goggles

Safety Sodium hydroxide pellets are corrosive. 4 mol dm^{-3} hydrochloric acid is irritant. Eye protection is essential. Use goggles NOT safety spectacles.

Method

Experiment 1

1. Using the measuring cylinder, transfer 25 cm^3 of water to the cup and measure its temperature.

2. Pour 25 cm^3 of hydrochloric acid into the measuring cylinder and measure its temperature.

3. Weigh out 4 g of sodium hydroxide pellets onto the watch glass and add the pellets to the water in the cup. Stir with the thermometer and measure the temperature when all of the pellets have dissolved.

4. Immediately add the 25 cm^3 of hydrochloric acid and measure the highest temperature whilst stirring with the thermometer.

Experiment 2

5. Repeat the procedure but interchange steps 3 and 4.

Sample results

Experiment 1

Temperature change for dissolution of NaOH = 45 °C

Temperature change for neutralisation by HCl = 7 °C

Experiment 2

Temperature change for dilution of HCl = 1 °C

Temperature change for neutralisation by NaOH = 31 °C

Calculations

Experiment 1

$\Delta H_{sol} = -(25 + 4) \div 1000 \times 4.2 \times 45 \div 0.1 = -54.81 \, \text{kJ/mol}$

$\Delta H_n = -(25 + 25 + 4) \div 1000 \times 4.2 \times 7 \div 0.1 = -15.88 \, \text{kJ/mol}$

Total enthalpy change = −70.69 kJ/mol

Experiment 2

$\Delta H_{dil} = -(25 + 25) \div 1000 \times 4.2 \times 1 \div 0.1 = -2.10 \, \text{kJ/mol}$

$\Delta H_n = -(25 + 25 + 4) \div 1000 \times 4.2 \times 31 \div 0.1 = -70.31 \, \text{kJ/mol}$

Total enthalpy change = −72.41 kJ/mol

Note

Within limits of acceptable experimental error, the results are consistent with Hess's Law which states: The net enthalpy change for a chemical reaction is independent of the path followed.

9.8 Using Hess's Law to determine the enthalpy of hydration for copper(II) sulfate(VI)

Anhydrous copper(II) sulfate(VI)
Copper(II) sulfate(VI) crystals
 ($CuSO_4.2H_2O$)
Spatula
Distilled water
Expanded polystyrene drinks cup

Thermometer
Measuring cylinder ($50\,cm^3$)
Top-pan balance
Scrap paper
Eye protection

Safety Copper(II) sulfate(VI) is harmful.

Method

1. Using the measuring cylinder, transfer $50\,cm^3$ of water to the cup and measure its temperature.

2. Weigh out 4 g of anhydrous copper(II) sulfate(VI) (0.025 mol) and add it to the water in the cup. Measure the highest temperature and find the temperature change.

3. Calculate the enthalpy change from:

   $\Delta H = mass \div 1000 \times 4.2 \times temperature\ change \div number\ of\ moles$

4. Repeat the procedure using 6.25 g of copper(II) sulfate(VI) crystals and $47.75\,cm^3$ of water (5×0.025 moles of water less to compensate for this amount of water of crystallisation in the hydrated copper(II) sulfate(VI)).

5. Use Hess's Law to find the enthalpy of hydration:

$$CuSO_4(s) \longrightarrow CuSO_4.5H_2O(s)$$
$$Cu^{2+}(aq) + SO_4^{2-}(aq)$$

Sample results

Temperature change when $CuSO_4$ dissolved $= +6\,°C$

Temperature change when $CuSO_4.5H_2O$ dissolved $= -2\,°C$

Calculations

$\Delta H_{sol}[CuSO_4] = (50 + 4) \div 1000 \times 4.2 \times -6 \div 0.025 = -54\,kJ/mol$

$\Delta H_{sol}[CuSO_4.5H_2O] = (47.75 + 6.25) \div 1000 \times 4.2 \times 2 \div 0.025$

$= +18.14\,kJ/mol$

$\Delta H_{hyd}[CuSO_4] = -54.43 - (+18.14) = -72.57\,kJ/mol$

9.9 Indirect determination of the enthalpy change for the thermal decomposition of calcium carbonate

Calcium carbonate	Polystyrene drinks cup
Calcium oxide	Thermometer
Spatula	Pipette
Top-pan balance	Pipette filler
Hydrochloric acid ($2\,mol\,dm^{-3}$)	Eye protection

Safety Hydrochloric acid is an irritant. Calcium oxide is irritant and reacts exothermically with water. Eye protection is essential. Risk of calcium carbonate spraying out acid during the reaction.

Method

1. Using the pipette and pipette filler, transfer $50\,cm^3$ of hydrochloric acid to the polystyrene drinks cup.

2. Measure the temperature of the acid every 5 seconds and then add $5\,g$ of calcium carbonate after 10–15 seconds.

3. Continue to measure the temperature every 5 seconds until there is no further change in temperature or the temperature begins to fall.

4. Take three more temperature measurements. And then discard the reaction mixture.

5. Plot a graph of temperature/ °C on the y-axis and time/min on the x-axis and find the change in temperature (ΔT) by extrapolation. (See Experiment 9.5, method step 6.)

6. Repeat the procedure using $2.8\,g$ of calcium oxide.

7. Calculate the enthalpy change for the reactions and hence calculate the enthalpy change for the thermal decomposition of calcium carbonate by applying Hess's Law.

Sample results

Time/s	Temperature/°C	
	Calcium carbonate	Calcium oxide
0	15.3	15.9
5	15.3	15.9
10	17.1	17.7
15	17.4	19.2
20	18.1	20.8
25	19.2	23.4
30	19.4	25.7
35	19.5	27.3
40	19.3	29.1
45	19.3	30.3
50	19.3	30.3
55	19.2	29.6
60	19.1	29.5
65	–	29.4
70	–	29.3
ΔT	4.7	15.9

Calculation

$\Delta H_r = \dfrac{\text{Mass} \times c \times \Delta T}{\text{No. of moles}}$ where c = specific heat capacity measured in kJ mol^{-1} K^{-1}, mass is measured in kg.

$\Delta H_r[CaCO_3 + HCl] = -\dfrac{0.055 \times 4.2 \times 4.7}{0.05} = -21.7 \, \text{kJ/mol}$

$\Delta H_r[CaO + HCl] = -\dfrac{0.0528 \times 4.2 \times 15.9}{0.05} = -70.5 \, \text{kJ/mol}$

By Hess's Law:

$$CaCO_3 \xrightarrow{\Delta H_2} CaO + CO_2$$

$\Delta H_1 \searrow$ HCl   HCl $\swarrow \Delta H_3$

$$CaCl_2 + H_2O + CO_2$$

$$\Delta H_1 = \Delta H_2 + \Delta H_3$$

$$\Delta H_2 = \Delta H_1 - \Delta H_3 = -21.7 - (-70.5) = +48.8 \, kJ/mol$$

Notes

1. The equations for the reactions are:

    $CaCO_3 + 2HCl \rightarrow CaCl_2 + CO_2 + H_2O$

    $CaO + 2HCl \rightarrow CaCl_2 + H_2O$

2. $50 \, cm^3$ of HCl is equivalent to $0.1 \, mol \, dm^{-3}$. Therefore $0.05 \, mol \, dm^{-3}$ of the two solids is required because the stoichiometry of the equations for the reactions is 1:2. This equates to $5 \, g$ of $CaCO_3$ and $2.8 \, g$ of CaO.

3. The work done by the carbon dioxide on the atmosphere has been ignored in calculating the enthalpy changes.

9.10 Enthalpy and volume changes associated with solvation

The following solids: lithium chloride, sodium chloride, potassium chloride, calcium chloride and anhydrous iron(III) chloride
Spatula
Top-pan balance
Polystyrene drinks cup

Thermometer
Measuring cylinder ($50 \, cm^3$)
Scrap paper
Two burettes ($50 \, cm^3$), one fitted with a bung
Distilled water

Safety Calcium chloride and iron(III) chloride are both irritant.

Method

Measuring enthalpy changes

1. Using the measuring cylinder, transfer $50 \, cm^3$ of distilled water to a polystyrene drinks cup.

2. Measure the temperature of the water.

3. Add the correct mass of solid to the distilled water to produce a $2 \, mol \, dm^{-3}$ solution.

4. Stir to dissolve with the thermometer and measure the temperature again.

5. Calculate the enthalpy change.

6. Repeat the procedure for each of the solids.

Measuring volume changes

1. Using a burette transfer $50\,cm^3$ of distilled water to another burette.

2. Record the reading on the burette.

3. Add the correct mass of solid to $50\,cm^3$ of distilled water in the burette to produce a $2\,mol\,dm^{-3}$ solution.

4. Close the burette with a bung and invert the burette several times until the solid completely dissolves.

5. Measure the total volume of the solution.

6. Calculate the volume of solid added from density data and add this to the $50\,cm^3$ of distilled water. This is the total volume of material before mixing.

7. Compare this theoretical result with the actual measured value.

Sample results

Solid	$\rho/g\,cm^3$	M_r	Mass to dissolve/g	Vol of solid dissolved/cm^3
LiCl	2.1	42.4	4.24	2.0
NaCl	2.2	58.4	5.84	2.7
KCl	2.0	74.6	7.46	3.7
$CaCl_2$	2.5	111.0	11.10	4.4
$FeCl_3$	2.8	162.0	16.20	5.8

Solid	ΔT	$\Delta H/kJ\,mol^{-1}$	Theoretical vol/ cm^3	Measured vol/cm^3	Δvol
LiCl	+13.1	− 29.8	52.0	51.6	− 0.4
NaCl	− 1.4	+ 3.3	52.7	52.4	− 0.3
KCl	− 7.4	+17.9	53.7	53.6	− 0.1
$CaCl_2$	+17.3	− 44.4	54.4	53.8	− 0.6
$FeCl_3$	+37.5	−104.3	55.8	56.1	− 1.7

Notes

1. The results show that as the number of electron shells in the ions increase, ΔH gets less exothermic and the bonds between ions and water particles get weaker. As the charge on the ions increases, ΔH gets more exothermic so the bonds get stronger.

2. Increased force of attraction between water particles and cations brings them closer together so the solution shrinks. Decreased force of attraction between water particles and the cations results in the particles not being so close together so the shrinkage is less.

3. In order to confirm the information already given in Note 1, more able students could plot:

   (i) number of electron shells in Li^+, Na^+ and K^+ against Δvol and also ΔH.

   (ii) ionic charge for K^+, Ca^{2+} and Fe^{3+} against Δvol and ΔH.

   (iii) ΔH against Δvol for all five solids.

10 ELECTROCHEMISTRY

Electrochemistry is the study of solutions of electrolytes and the phenomena occurring at electrodes immersed in such solutions. Electrolytes are substances which, in the molten state or dissolved in water, will conduct an electric current. The decomposition of an electrolyte by the passage of an electric current is known as electrolysis.

The materials through which current enters and leaves the electrolyte are called electrodes. The positive electrode is called the anode and the negative electrode is called the cathode.

An electric current is the flow of charge through a conductor. Conventional current flows from positive to negative. Electron current flows from negative to positive. In solid conductors the charge carriers are electrons. In liquids the charge carriers are ions.

For an electrolyte to conduct, its ions must be free to move. Nothing moves without a force acting on it. The force which causes the charge carriers to move is the electromotive force which is measured in volts.

10.1 Electrical conductivity of sodium chloride solution

This experiment is in four parts.

10.1.1 Effect of concentration

Two graphite rods (10 cm) mounted in a rubber bung
Retort stand and clamp
Two crocodile clips
Three connecting wires with a 4 mm plug at each end. Ammeter (0–1 A)
6 V dc power supply

Measuring cylinder (100 cm³)
Distilled water
Sodium chloride solution (1 mol dm⁻³)
Beaker (250 cm³)
Absorbent paper tissues
Eye protection

Safety Chlorine gas is toxic. Avoid inhaling chlorine. Do not let the current flow for more time than is needed to take readings. This experiment should be carried out in a well ventilated area because of the possible production of chlorine.

Method

1. Set up the apparatus as shown below:

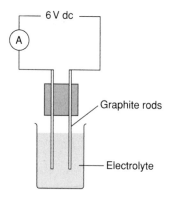

Figure 10.1 Measuring the electrical conductivity of an electrolyte.

2. Using the measuring cylinder, prepare sodium chloride solutions with the following concentrations by appropriately diluting the $1 \, \text{mol dm}^{-3}$ solution with distilled water:

Molar concentration	NaCl/cm³	Distilled water/cm³
0.2	20	80
0.4	40	60
0.6	60	40
0.8	80	20
1.0	100	0

3. Pour each solution in turn into the beaker, lower the electrodes into the solution to the same depth each time, swirl the beaker and measure the current flowing.

4. Before changing solutions, wash the electrodes by lowering them into a beaker of distilled water, swirl the beaker and then wipe the electrodes dry with absorbent paper tissues. This prevents contamination from the previous solution.

5. Plot a line graph of concentration of NaCl/mol per dm³ on the x-axis and current/A on the y-axis.

Sample results

Electrodes 0.5 cm apart immersed 3.5 cm.

NaCl/mol dm^{-3}	Current/A
0.2	0.10
0.4	0.16
0.6	0.21
0.8	0.24
1.0	0.27

Notes

1. Prolonged electrical contact between electrodes and electrolyte will cause electrolysis and hydrogen will be liberated at the cathode and chlorine will be liberated at the anode. This will decrease the concentration of chloride ions and increase the concentration of sodium ions so the current readings should be taken quickly.

2. The results show that increasing the concentration of sodium chloride solution increases the conductivity because there are more ions present to carry the charge.

10.1.2 Effect of temperature

Additional apparatus needed:

Bunsen burner   Thermometer
Tripod and gauze   Beaker (100 cm^3)

Safety As for 10.1.1.

Method

1. Carry out the procedure given in 10.1.1 using 1 mol dm^{-3} sodium chloride solution and repeat for a range of temperatures.

2. Use the Bunsen burner, tripod and gauze to heat the solution to a few degrees above the required temperature and measure the current flowing.

3. Plot a line graph of temperature/ °C on the x-axis and current/A on the y-axis.

Sample results

Electrodes 0.5 cm apart immersed 5 cm in 1 mol dm^{-3} NaCl.

Temp/°C	Current/A
18	0.38
35	0.47
47	0.55
60	0.62
73	0.66

Note

The results show that increasing the temperature increased the conductivity because the migrating ions reached their destination quicker at higher temperatures.

10.1.3 Effect of surface area of contact between the electrodes and electrolyte

Additional apparatus needed:

Ruler

Triangular cross-section file

Safety As for 10.1.1.

Method

1. Using the edge of the file and a ruler, put scratch marks 1 cm apart down the full length of the electrode.

2. Repeat the procedure given in 10.1.1 using 1 mol dm^{-3} NaCl but immerse the electrodes at different depths using the scratch marks as a guide. Begin with the electrodes just touching the surface of the electrolyte (0.1 cm).

3. Plot a line graph of depth to which the electrodes were immersed/cm on the x-axis and current/A on the y-axis.

Sample results

Electrodes 0.5 mm apart in $1 \, mol \, dm^{-3}$ NaCl.

Electrode depth/cm	Current/A
0.1	0.05
1.0	0.16
2.0	0.22
3.0	0.28
4.0	0.35
5.0	0.38

Notes

1. Note 1 in 10.1.1. applies to this activity.

2. The deeper the electrodes are immersed, the greater the area of contact with the electrolyte.

3. Conductivity increases with area of contact with the electrolyte because there is more surface area in contact with the ions.

4. More able students should plot surface area against current/mA. Surface area is calculated from $\pi \times d \times l$ where d = diameter of the graphite rod and l = depth of immersion.

10.1.4 Effect of distance between the electrodes

Additional apparatus needed:

A 400 cm³ beaker

A wooden electrode holder constructed as follows: Cut a piece of 1 cm square cross-section wood 12 cm long. Using a triangular-shaped file, make six notches with the shoulders of adjacent notches 1 cm apart along the length of the piece of wood starting 2 cm from one end. The notches should be the same size at their widest point as the diameter of the electrodes. Hold the electrodes in place in the notches using a rubber band (see Figure 10.2).

Safety As for 10.1.1.

Figure 10.2 Electrode holder.

Method

1. Use the procedure given in Experiment 10.1.1 using $1\,mol\,dm^{-3}$ NaCl solution with two graphite rod electrodes.

2. Take current readings with the electrodes in notches 1 and 2, 1 and 3, 1 and 4, 1 and 5, and 1 and 6. This corresponds to distances of 1–5 cm between the electrodes.

3. Plot a line graph of distance between electrodes/cm on the x-axis and current/A on the y-axis.

Sample results

Electrodes immersed 5 cm in $1\,mol\,dm^{-3}$ NaCl .

Distance/cm	Current/A
1	0.36
2	0.29
3	0.26
4	0.23
5	0.19

Notes

1. Note 1 in 10.1.1 applies.

2. Filing the notches in the electrode holder will be made easier if you clamp the piece of wood to the bench using a G-clamp.

3. Ensure the depth to which the electrodes are immersed remains constant throughout the experiment.

4. The current decreases as the electrodes are placed further apart because the ions have further to travel to their respective destinations and encounter more obstruction in doing so.

10.2 Electrophoresis of potassium manganate(VII)

Microscope slide
Two crocodile clips
Two connecting wires with 4 mm plugs at each end
Filter paper
Scissors

Two optical pins
Sodium chloride solution ($1\,mol\,dm^{-3}$)
Potassium manganate(VII)
Pencil and ruler
20 V dc power supply

Safety Potassium manganate(VII) is an oxidising agent and harmful. Students should not be allowed to use power packs which supply high voltage at more than 5 mA dc on short circuit.

Method

1. Cut a piece of filter paper the same size as the microscope slide.
2. Draw a thin pencil line midway across the piece of filter paper.
3. Moisten the filter paper with sodium chloride solution and place the moist filter paper on the microscope slide.
4. Hold the optical pins in place with crocodile clips and connect them to the power supply set at 20 V dc.
5. Using forceps, place one crystal of potassium manganate(VII) on the pencil line and switch on the power supply.
6. Observe the stain made by the potassium manganate(VII) crystal over a period of 30 minutes.

Sample results

The purple stain on the filter paper slowly spreads towards the positive electrode with a drift velocity of approximately : $10^{-5}\,\mathrm{m\,s^{-1}}$.

Notes

1. The sodium chloride solution improves the conductivity of the potassium manganate(VII).
2. The optical pins ensure good electrical contact across the whole width of the filter paper.
3. The potassium manganate(VII) dissociates into positively charged potassium ions and negatively charged manganate(VII) ions. The positively charged ions migrate towards the negative electrode and the negatively charged ions migrate towards the positive electrode.
4. More able students could extend the experiment by repeating it using different voltages and calculating the speed of migration of the manganate(VII) ion under the influence of different voltages.
5. At A-level the students could extend the experiment using additional apparatus and estimate the number of ions which moved from the relationship: $I = nAve$ where I = current/A, n = number of free ions per unit volume, v = average drift velocity of the ions/$\mathrm{m\,s^{-1}}$, A = cross-sectional area of the moist filter paper/$\mathrm{m^2}$ and e = charge on electron.

10.3 Electrolysis of copper(II) chromate(VI)

Copper(II) sulfate(VI) solution
    ($1\,mol\,dm^{-3}$)
Potassium chromate solution
    ($1\,mol\,dm^{-3}$)
Measuring cylinder ($50\,cm^3$)
Conical flask ($250\,cm^3$)
Filter paper
Funnel
Spatula
Concentrated sulfuric(VI) acid
Teat pipette (dropper)
U-tube

Protective gloves

Graphite rods
Two crocodile clips
Ammeter
Rheostat
Four connecting wires with $4\,mm$
    plugs at each end
$12\,V$ dc power supply
Sheet of white paper or white tile
Distilled water
Agar
Eye protection

Safety Concentrated sulfuric(VI) acid is corrosive. Copper(II) sulfate(VI) is harmful. Potassium chromate(VI) is very toxic and a category 2 carcinogen. It may cause skin sensitisation. Agar powder is harmful when inhaled. Eye protection is essential and gloves desirable.

Method

1. Mix $5\,cm^3$ of copper(II) sulfate(VI) solution with $50\,cm^3$ of potassium chromate(VI) solution and filter. Collect the filtrate in a conical flask and discard it.

2. Using the spatula, transfer the precipitate to a $100\,cm^3$ beaker and add $25\,cm^3$ of distilled water.

3. Add concentrated sulfuric(VI) acid, dropwise, until the precipitate dissolves.

4. Warm the solution and add $2.5\,g$ of agar.

5. Stir with a glass rod and transfer the mixture to a U-tube, close the open ends of the U-tube with bungs containing the graphite rods and set it aside to gel.

5. Set up the circuit shown in Figure 10.3 and pass a current of $0.05\,A$ (approximately $12\,V$).

Sample results

After 30 minutes, the area around the cathode turns blue and the area around the anode turns orange/brown.

Notes

1. The partition will be seen more easily if the U-tube is placed in front of a piece of white paper or white tile.

2. The results show that blue positive hydrated copper(II) ions migrate towards the negative electrode and yellow negative chromate(VI) ions migrate towards the positive electrode.

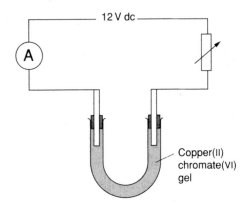

Figure 10.3 Electrolysis of a copper(II) chromate(VI) gel in a U-tube.

3. Higher current will cause too much turbulence in the electrolyte and destroy the effect.

10.4 Products of electrolysis from different electrolytes using graphite electrodes

Plastic margarine tub
Two graphite electrodes
Two size 13 rubber bungs bored out to take the graphite rods
No. 9 cork borer
Solutions of : Copper(II) sulfate(VI), copper(II) chloride, sodium chloride(1 mol dm^{-3} each), distilled water acidified with a drop of concentrated sulfuric(VI) acid

Four connecting wires with 4 mm plugs at each end
Two crocodile clips
6 V dc power supply
Ammeter (0–1 A)
Rheostat
Test-tubes
Blue litmus paper
Splints
Two wooden blocks (5 × 5 × 10 cm)
Eye protection

Safety Concentrated sulfuric(VI) acid is corrosive. $1\,mol\,dm^{-3}$ Copper(II) sulfate(VI) and copper(II) chloride are both harmful. Do not continue the electrolysis for longer than is necessary to test the product. Avoid inhaling chlorine. Work in a well ventilated area.

Method

1. Using the cork borer, cut two holes in the bottom of the plastic tub.

2. Insert the graphite rods into the holes in the bungs and fit the bungs into the holes in the plastic tub.

3. Fill the tub with electrolyte and place the tub on the two wooden blocks.

4. Fill two test-tubes with electrolyte, cover the top with your finger, invert the test-tube under the electrolyte in the tub and remove your finger. The test-tubes should retain the electrolyte. Place the inverted test-tubes containing the electrolyte over the graphite rods. See Figure 10.4.

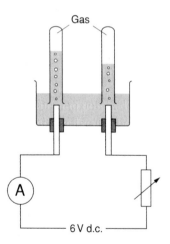

Figure 10.4 Collecting gases from electrolysis.

5. Connect the electrodes to the circuit described in Figure 10.4 and adjust the current to 1 A.

6. Test the gas produced at the cathode for the presence of hydrogen using a burning splint.

7. Test the gas produced at the anode firstly with damp blue litmus paper and secondly with a glowing splint.

Sample results

Electrolyte	Products	
	Cathode	Anode
Sodium chloride	Hydrogen	Chlorine
Copper(II) chloride	Copper	Chlorine
Copper(II) sulfate(VI)	Copper	Oxygen
Acidified water	Hydrogen	Oxygen

Notes

1. Graphite rods are inert so they do not react with the products of electrolysis (unless oxygen is formed, in which case CO_2 may be obtained). The rods being black should show up clearly any deposit on them.

2. Hydrogen gives a squeaky pop when a burning splint is placed in a test tube of the gas.

3. Oxygen will rekindle a glowing splint.

4. Chlorine bleaches litmus.

10.5 Electrolysis of copper(II) sulfate(VI) solution using copper electrodes

Copper(II) sulfate(VI) solution
   $(1\,mol\,dm^{-3})$
6 V dc power supply
Two crocodile clips
Four connecting wires with 4 mm
   plugs at each end.
Ammeter (0–1 A)
Rheostat

Two copper electrodes $(1 \times 5\,cm)$
Scourer
Aqueous ammonia solution
   $(2\,mol\,dm^{-3})$
Propanone
Two beakers $(100\,cm^3)$
Top-pan balance
Eye protection

Safety $1\,mol\,dm^{-3}$ copper(II) sulfate(VI) is harmful. Propanone is highly flammable. Ammonia is toxic and the vapour can cause an asthma attack in susceptible people but the concentration will be relatively low.

Method

1. Dip the electrodes in the aqueous ammonia and clean them using the scourer. Rinse the electrodes under a running tap and then swirl them in a beaker of propanone. Remove them from the propanone and wave them in the air until dry.

2. Mark the electrodes positive and negative by making an impression on the surface at the top of the electrode using a ball-point pen.

3. Weigh the electrodes, hold them against the internal surface of the beaker, fold over the top 1 cm of the electrode and hook over the lip of the beaker so that they hang in place opposite each other. Add the electrolye to the beaker so that the electrodes are immersed to between 3 and 4 cm. Use crocodile clips to connect the electrodes in the circuit and adjust the current to 1 A using the rheostat.

4. After 25 minutes switch off the current, remove the electrodes, swirl them gently in a beaker of water and then in a beaker of propanone. Wipe off any copper(II) oxide from the anode using an absorbent paper tissue before washing and drying.

5. Wave them in the air to dry them and then re-weigh.

Sample results

	Before	After	Change in mass/g
Mass of cathode/g	1.75	1.80	+0.50
Mass of anode/g	1.68	1.63	−0.50

Notes

1. During the electrolysis of aqueous copper(II) sulfate(VI) solution using copper electrodes the anode loses mass by copper dissolving in the electrolyte and the cathode gains mass by the same amount of copper being deposited.

2. The reactions at the electrodes are:

   At the cathode: $Cu^{2+} + 2e^- \rightarrow Cu^0$

   At the anode: $Cu^0 \rightarrow Cu^{2+} + 2e^-$

3. The results show that the mass gained by the cathode = the mass lost by the anode.

4. The intensity of the colour of the solution remains constant.

5. Treat the cathode gently with the final washing and drying because there is the possibility of losing some of the deposited copper.

10.6 Factors affecting the mass of copper deposited during electrolysis

Apparatus/reagents as for 10.5.

Safety As for 10.5.

Method

1. As for 10.5 but carry out all measurements on the anode only. This will avoid the problem of the deposited copper on the cathode falling off during rinsing and drying when the deposits are heavy.

2. Use the loss in mass of the anode to study the mass of copper transferred.

10.6.1 Effect of time

Sample results

$1\,mol\,dm^{-3}$ $CuSO_4$ solution at $1\,A$

Time/min	Mass of copper/g
2.5	0.05
5.0	0.10
10.0	0.20
15.0	0.31
20.0	0.40

10.6.2 Effect of current flowing

Sample results

$1\,mol\,dm^{-3}$ $CuSO_4$ solution for 10 minutes

Current/A	Mass of copper/g
0.2	0.04
0.4	0.08
0.6	0.12
0.8	0.16
1.0	0.40

10.6.3 Effect of charge on the ions

Rheostat

Ammeter (0–1 A)

Two beakers (100 cm³)

Bunsen burner

Tripod and gauze

Thermometer

Four copper foil electrodes
(1 cm × 5 cm)

Five connecting wires with 4 mm plugs
at each end

Four crocodile clips

Scourer

Top-pan balance

Propanone

Aqueous ammonia (2 mol dm⁻³)

Copper(II) sulfate(VI) solution
(0.5 mol dm⁻³)

Solution containing 100 g NaCl +
1 g NaOH per dm³

Eye protection

Safety Propanone is highly flammable. Ammonia is toxic and the vapour can cause an asthma attack in susceptible people but the concentration will be relatively low. Solid sodium hydroxide is corrosive.

Method

1. Clean all electrodes using the method given in 10.5.

2. Weigh the electrodes.

3. Set up the apparatus as shown in Figure 10.5.

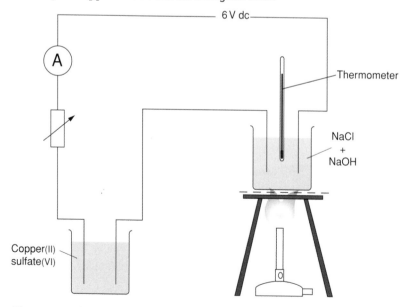

Figure 10.5 Electrolysis of solutions involving copper(I) and copper(II) ions.

4. Heat the sodium chloride–sodium hydroxide mixture to 80 °C.

5. Adjust the current flowing to 0.5 A and let the electrolysis take place for 15 minutes (900 s), swirling the anodes to prevent the build-up of copper(II) oxide.

6. Wash and dry the anodes as described in 10.5 and reweigh them.

Results

	Cu(I)	Cu(II)
Initial mass/g	1.73	1.64
Final mass/g	1.43	1.49
Mass of copper transferred/g	0.30	0.15
Charge on the ions	1+	2+

Notes

1. The mass of an element liberated or deposited during electrolysis is directly proportional to the charge flowing.

2. The mole fraction of an element liberated or deposited during electrolysis is inversely proportional to the charge on the ions.

10.7 Anodising aluminium

Two aluminium strips (1×10 cm)
Beaker (250 cm^3)
Three beakers (100 cm^3)
Two crocodile clips
Sulfuric(VI) acid (2 mol dm^{-3})
Sodium hydroxide solution
    (2 mol dm^{-3})
Propanone
Absorbent paper tissue
12 V dc power supply

Forceps
Bunsen burner
Tripod and gauze
Dylon cold fabric dye
Measuring cylinder (500 cm^3)
Distilled water
Concentrated ethanoic acid
Teat pipette (dropper)
Beaker of boiling water
Eye protection

Safety Concentrated ethanoic acid, 2 mol dm^{-3} sulfuric(VI) acid and 2 mol dm^{-3} sodium hydroxide are all corrosive. Propanone is highly flammable. Handle the anode using forceps to avoid being scalded by boiling water.

Method

1. Degrease the strips of aluminium by swirling them in propanone and wipe them dry with absorbent paper tissue.

2. Remove the existing oxide layer from the strips by immersing them in a beaker of sodium hydroxide solution until they begin to effervesce. Remove with forceps. Rinse them under a cold running tap.

3. Assemble the apparatus as described for 10.1 but use the aluminium strips as electrodes, sulfuric(VI) acid as the electrolyte, use a 12 V dc power supply and omit the ammeter.

4. Allow the current to flow for 20 minutes.

5. Remove the anode and rinse it under a running tap.

6. Dissolve the contents of one capsule of dye in $500 \, cm^3$ of distilled water and add a few drops of concentrated ethanoic acid.

7. Transfer some of the dye solution to a $100 \, cm^3$ beaker and heat on the tripod and gauze over the Bunsen burner.

8. Transfer the anode to the beaker of hot dye and leave it for 20 minutes.

9. Transfer the anode to a beaker of boiling water and continue boiling for 20 minutes to seal the colour and make it permanent.

Notes

1. Anodising is a controlled corrosion process in which the layer of oxide builds up on the metal surface and prevents the metal from further oxidation.

$$4OH^- - 4e^- \rightarrow 2H_2O + O_2$$

$$4Al + 3O_2 \rightarrow 2Al_2O_3$$

2. Equation for the reaction involving removal of the oxide layer:

$$Al_2O_3 + 2NaOH + 3H_2O \rightarrow 2NaAl(OH)_4$$

3. · The Al_2O_3 layer which builds up during the electrolysis is porous. In aqueous solution, it reacts with water:

$$Al_2O_3 + H_2O \rightarrow Al_2O_3H^+ + OH^-$$

The dye contains a coloured anion which associates with the $Al_2O_3H^+$ ion. When the anode is immersed in boiling water, a $Al_2O_3H_2O$ seal is formed over the pores of the spongy oxide layer in which the coloured anions are trapped.

4. The electrodes are best held in place by bending one end and hooking them over the lip of the beaker.

10.8 Producing electricity from a chemical reaction

Beaker (100 cm^3)
Copper foil (5 cm × 1 cm)
Magnesium ribbon (5 cm)
Sulfuric(VI) acid (1 mol dm^{-3})

1.5 V torch bulb in a holder connected to two wires with crocodile clips attached

Eye protection

Safety Magnesium ribbon is highly flammable. 1 mol dm^{-3} sulfuric(VI) acid is irritant.

Method

1. Place the copper foil and magnesium ribbon inside the beaker and bend the ends over the lip of the beaker so that they hang in place opposite each other.

2. Connect the wires from the bulb holder to the metals using the crocodile clips.

3. Fill the beaker with sulfuric(VI) acid and observe the reaction of the magnesium in the acid.

4. Observe what happens to the torch bulb.

5. Observe what happens to the copper foil.

Sample results

The bulb lights up showing that electricity has been produced.

Bubbles of gas collect around the copper foil and the light gets dim.

The magnesium ribbon dissolves which is accompanied by effervescence.

Notes

1. An electrochemical cell is a cell in which a chemical reaction takes place and some of the energy is released in the form of electrical energy.

2. The magnesium quickly dissolves and the bulb ceases to light when the reaction is over (approximately 90 s).

3. The bubbles of gas which form on the surface of the copper are hydrogen. The electrons which pass from the magnesium to the copper through the external circuit reduce hydrogen ions to gaseous hydrogen. This is called polarisation and is a problem with this type of cell.

4. The hydrogen obstructs the flow of current by causing poor electrical contact between copper and the solution and this explains the bulb getting dim.

5. The cell reactions are:

$$Mg^{2+} \rightarrow Mg^0 + 2e^-$$

$$2H^+ + 2e^- \rightarrow H_2$$

10.9 Measuring cell emf

High resistance voltmeter (0–1 V) or CRO

Rheostat

Ammeter (0–100 mA)

Five connecting leads with 4 mm plugs at each end

Daniell cell (see Note 4)

Safety Copper(II) sulfate(VI) for the Daniell cell is harmful.

Method

1. Assemble the apparatus according to the circuit shown in Figure 10.6.

2. Change the resistance of the circuit by adjusting the rheostat and take voltage readings for a range of current flowing.

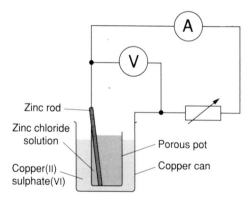

Figure 10.6 Measuring cell emf.

3. Plot a line graph of pd/V on the x-axis and current/mA on the y-axis.

4. Extrapolate the line to zero current. This gives the emf of the cell.

Sample results

Current/mA	pd/V	Current/mA	pd/V
20	1.02	70	0.74
30	0.97	80	0.62
40	0.92	90	0.53
50	0.87	100	0.42
60	0.82		

Notes

1. Increasing the resistance of the circuit decreased the current flowing.

2. The pd increased as the resistance of the circuit increased.

3. The cell emf is the pd at infinite external resistance.

4. A Daniell cell can be made by placing a porous pot containing a zinc rod immersed in $1 \, mol \, dm^{-3}$ $ZnSO_4$ solution in a copper can containing $1 \, mol \, dm^{-3}$ $CuSO_4$ solution. The copper can is the positive electrode and the zinc rod, the negative. The cell emf = 1.1 V which should coincide with the pd at zero current on the extrapolated graph.

5. If a CRO is used in place of the voltmeter then it should be calibrated beforehand so that full-scale deflection is equivalent to 1.5 V.

10.10 Investigating the effect of different electrode combinations on the voltage produced by an electrochemical cell

Aqueous sodium chloride solution ($1 \, mol \, dm^{-3}$)
Metal foils: magnesium, aluminium, copper, lead, zinc and nickel
Beaker ($250 \, cm^3$)

Two connecting wires with 4 mm plugs at one end and crocodile clips on the other
Voltmeter (0–1 V and 0–5 V dual range)

Safety Magnesium is highly flammable. Lead metal is low hazard but hands should be washed after handling it because lead compounds are toxic.

Method

Fill the beaker with sodium chloride solution and measure the voltage produced by immersing different combinations of electrodes in it.

Sample results

Voltage (volts) produced by various combinations of electrodes immersed in $1\,mol\,dm^{-3}$ NaCl:

	Mg	Al	Cu	Pb	Zn	Ni
Mg	0	0.7	1.4	1.1	1.0	0.8
Al	0.7	0	0.7	0.4	0.1	0.7
Cu	1.4	0.7	0	0 5	0.7	0.2
Pb	1.1	0.4	0.3	0	0.4	0.1
Zn	1.0	0.1	0.7	0.5	0	0.7
Ni	0.8	0.7	0.1	0.3	0.7	0

Notes

1. Electrochemical cells consist of two electrodes of different materials (usually metals) immersed in a solution of an electrolyte.

2. The combination of metals with the biggest difference in reactivity between them gives the highest voltage.

3. More able students could use the data to establish an electrochemical series for the metals.

10.11 Effect of concentration of electrolyte on the voltage of an electrochemical cell

Additional apparatus needed:
Sodium chloride solution
   ($1\,mol\,dm^{-3}$)
Copper foil and magnesium ribbon
Beaker ($250\,cm^3$)
Distilled water

Two connecting wires with 4 mm plugs at one end and crocodile clips on the other
Voltmeter (0–1 V and 0–5 V dual range)
Measuring cylinder ($250\,cm^3$)

Safety Magnesium is highly flammable.

Method

1. Carry out the procedure given in 10.9 using copper foil and magnesium ribbon as the electrodes.

2. Repeat the procedure with the electrolyte diluted 1/10, 1/100, 1/1 000 and 1/10 000.

3. Plot a line graph of dilution on the x-axis (each dilution factor = one large square) and voltage on the y-axis.

Results

Dilution	Voltage/V
1.0	1.4
0.1	1.2
0.01	1.0
0.001	0.6
0.0001	0.4

Notes

1. The dilutions are best done successively by taking $25\,cm^3$ of the electrolyte and diluting to $250\,cm^3$ with distilled water using the measuring cylinder.

2. From the Nernst equation, the cell emf is proportional to the logarithm of the ionic concentration of the electrolyte.

3. There is a linear relationship between voltage and dilution to the power of 10 for the electrolyte.

4. Decreasing the concentration of the electrolyte decreases the cell emf because there are fewer particles to react.

5. More able students should plot voltage against $\log_{10}$ of concentration in $mol\,dm^{-3}$ (dilution).

6. The experiment could be extended by investigating the effect of temperature and the depth of immersion of the electrodes and also the distance between them (see Experiment 10.1.2–10.1.4). Temperature effects will be in the order of $0.2\,V$. Expect effects of distance between, and depth to which the electrodes are immersed, to be in the order of $0.3\,V$. Therefore meters with full scale deflection of $1\,V$ are needed in order to detect these changes.

7. Temperature effects can be explained using kinetic theory, depth of immersion and distance apart can be interpreted in terms of their effect on resistance.

10.12 Measurement of electrode potentials

Copper, zinc, nickel and iron foils and magnesium ribbon

Solutions (1 mol dm^{-3}) of copper(II) sulfate(VI), zinc sulfate(VI), nickel sulfate(VI), magnesium sulfate(VI) and iron(II) sulfate(VI)

Hydrochloric acid (1 mol dm^{-3})

Beakers (100 cm^3)

Saturated potassium chloride solution

Filter paper

Scissors

Crocodile clips

Connecting wires with 4 mm plugs at each end

High resistance voltmeter

Scourer

Apparatus for generating hydrogen (see Chapter 16)

Hydrogen electrode (see Figure 10.7)

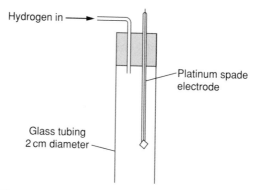

Figure 10.7 The hydrogen electrode.

Safety Hydrochloric acid, copper and nickel salts are irritants. Iron(II) salts are harmful. Hydrogen–air mixtures are explosive. Magnesium foil is highly flammable.

Method

1. Clean the metal foils with the scourer and rinse under a cold running tap.

2. Immerse the metal foil in the aqueous solution of its ions in a beaker and secure it by folding the end of the foil over the lip of the beaker. Hold it in place with a crocodile clip.

3. Immerse the hydrogen electrode in a beaker of hydrochloric acid and connect it to the hydrogen supply.

4. Soak a strip of filter paper in saturated potassium chloride solution to form a salt bridge and immerse one end in one solution and the other end in the other solution.

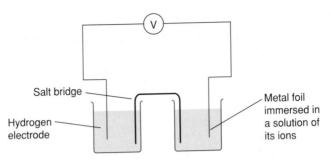

Figure 10.8 Measuring cell emf.

5. Connect the electrodes to the voltmeter and measure the voltage as the hydrogen bubbles through the hydrogen electrode. If the voltmeter reads < 0 reverse the connecting leads and change the sign.

6. Repeat the procedure for each of the metals immersed in the solution of its ions.

7. Measure the voltage of cells made up from various combinations of the metal foils immersed in solutions of their ions and compare the results with the expected voltage calculated from the measured electrode potentials.

Sample results

Electrode system	Electrode potential/v	
	Measured	Published value
$Mg^{2+} + 2e^- \rightarrow Mg$	−2.04	−2.37
$Zn^{2+} + 2e^- \rightarrow Zn$	−0.67	−0.76
$Cu^{2+} + 2e^- \rightarrow Cu$	0.37	0.34
$Fe^{2+} + 2e^- \rightarrow Fe$	−0.37	−0.44
$Ni^{2+} + 2e^- \rightarrow Ni$	−0.27	−0.25

Electrode combination	Cell emf/V	
	Calculated	Measured
$Zn \mid Zn^{2+} : Cu^{2+} \mid Cu$	1.04	1.00
$Mg \mid Mg^{2+} : Ni^{2+} \mid Ni$	1.77	1.50
$Zn \mid Zn^{2+} : Fe^{2+} \mid Fe$	0.30	0.25
$Ni \mid Ni^{2+} : Cu^{2+} \mid Cu$	0.64	0.42

Notes

1. An electrode consists of a metal in equilibrium with an aqueous solution of its ions.

2. By convention, a hydrogen electrode has an electrode potential of zero.

3. By convention cell emfs have a positive value. The more electronegative electrode is written on the left and the less electronegative one on the right so that electrons flow from left to right. When calculating cell emfs, subtract the right-hand electrode potential from the left-hand one, for example,

$$Zn \,|\, Zn^{2+} : Cu^{2+} \,|\, Cu$$

$$E = 0.34 - (-0.76) = 1.10\,V$$

4. Electrode equations are written as reduction processes.

11 REDOX

Reduction-oxidation reactions or redox for short involve electron transfer. Atoms or ions which gain electrons become reduced. Atoms or ions which lose electrons become oxidised. Reduction and oxidation take place simultaneously in the same reaction. Electrons have to come from somewhere and go somewhere. They cannot materialise and then disappear. A more reactive element has a greater tendency to become oxidised than a less reactive element. Therefore a more reactive element will displace a less reactive element from a solution of its ions or compound. The reactivity of an element depends upon the ease with which electrons are transferred.

11.1 Spontaneous atmospheric oxidation of nitrogen monoxide

For apparatus/reagents, see Chapter 16 section 16.4, plus eye protection, access to fume cupboard.

Safety This demonstration should be done in a fume cupboard because nitrogen dioxide is very toxic and corrosive. Eye protection is essential.

Method

1. Prepare a gas jar of nitrogen monoxide according to the method descibed in 16.4.

2. Place the gas jar of nitrogen monoxide in a fume cupboard, remove the lid and observe what happens.

Sample results

The colourless nitrogen monoxide spontaneously oxidises to brown nitrogen dioxide as it diffuses from the gas jar.

Notes

1. The equation for the reaction is:

    $$2NO + O_2 \rightarrow 2NO_2$$

11.2 Putting metals in a reactivity order by studying displacement reactions

Aqueous solutions ($1\,mol\,dm^{-3}$) of:
magnesium sulfate(VI), zinc
sulfate(VI), lead(II) nitrate(V) and
copper(II) sulfate(VI)

$5 \times 0.5\,cm$ strips of the metals:
magnesium, zinc, lead, copper

Hydrochloric acid ($2\,mol\,dm^{-3}$)
16 test-tubes in a rack
Emery cloth
Propanone
Absorbent paper tissues
Eye protection

Safety $2\,mol\,dm^{-3}$ hydrochloric acid is irritant. $1\,mol\,dm^{-3}$ copper(II) sulfate(VI) is harmful. Lead(II) nitrate(V) is toxic. The effects are cumulative. Pregnant women or younger pupils should not handle this substance. There is the danger of damage to the unborn child. Propanone is highly flammable. Hands must be washed thoroughly after handling lead foil because lead compounds are toxic.

Method

1. Remove any grease and corrosion from the metals using propanone and a scouring pad.

2. Rinse the metals with distilled water and blot them dry with absorbent paper tissue.

3. Put the different metals in solutions of different metal ions for 15 minutes and observe any changes which take place.

Sample results

Metals	$MgSO_4$	$ZnSO_4$	Solutions $Pb(NO_3)_2$	$CuSO_4$	HCl
Mg	–	Mg displaced Zn	Mg displaced Pb	Mg displaced Cu	Mg displaced H_2
Zn	no reaction	–	Zn displaced Pb	Zn displaced Cu	Zn displaced H_2
Pb	no reaction	no reaction	–	Pb displaced Cu	Pb displaced H_2
Cu	no reaction	no reaction	no reaction	–	no reaction

Notes

1. From the results, the order of reactivity of the elements is:

   $Mg > Zn > Pb > H > Cu$

2. Equations for the reactions that took place are of the type:

$$Mg^0(s) + Zn^{2+}(aq) \rightarrow Mg^{2+}(aq) + Zn^0(s)$$

3. The displacement of hydrogen from the acid by lead takes place very slowly and the reaction stops due to the formation of insoluble lead chloride, which coats the metal making it less susceptible to further attack by the acid. Look for bubbles of the gas forming on the metal surface together with a white deposit.

11.3 Comparing the reactivity of the alkali metals by observing their reaction with water

Lithium

Sodium

Potassium

Scalpel

Forceps

White ceramic tile

Absorbent paper tissues

Trough containing water

Wooden splints

Safety screens

Eye protection

Safety Alkali metals are highly flammable and corrosive by reacting with moisture to form strong alkalis, so the metals should be handled using forceps. This experiment must be performed behind safety screens to protect both teacher and students. Do not use potassium which has a yellow crust. Place safety screens as close to the trough as possible to prevent pieces of metal flying over the top. Students should wear eye protection. Do not attempt to confine the sodium or potassium in any way. Use fresh, cold water for each metal.

Method

1. Remove the metals one at a time from the oil in which they are kept using forceps.

2. Cut a 3 mm cube of the metal for potassium, a 4 mm cube for sodium and a 5 mm cube for lithium, and blot them dry with absorbent paper tissue. Lithium is difficult to cut.

3. Put the piece of metal in the trough of water and observe the reaction.

4. Hold a burning splint over the reacting metal to ignite the hydrogen which is produced.

Sample results

Metal	Observations
Lithium	Gentle reaction and red flame
Sodium	Vigorous reaction and yellow flame
Potassium	Violent reaction and spontaneous lilac flame

Notes

1. The results show a reactivity order of:

   $K > Na > Li$

2. Equations for the reactions:

   $2Li + 2H_2O \rightarrow 2LiOH + H_2$

   $2Na + 2H_2O \rightarrow 2NaOH + H_2$

   $2K + 2H_2O \rightarrow 2KOH + H_2$

3. The metals become oxidised by losing their outer electron. The bigger the atom, the more readily the electron is lost because the distance between the nucleus of the atom and the outer electron shell increases (inverse square law). Also the greater the number of inner electron shells , the greater the screening effect between the nuclear charge and the outer electron. Therefore reactivity increases on descending group I.

11.4 Comparing the reactivity of magnesium, zinc and iron by displacement of hydrogen from steam

Magnesium ribbon
Iron filings
Zinc powder
Spatula
Mineral wool
Distilled water
Retort stand and clamp

Bunsen burner
Three test-tubes with holes as shown
    in Figure 11.1, fitted with bungs
Matches
Safety screens
Eye protection

Safety Magnesium ribbon is highly flammable. Zinc powder is flammable. The demonstrations should be done behind a safety screen. Eye protection is essential.

Method

1. Assemble the apparatus as shown in Figure 11.1.

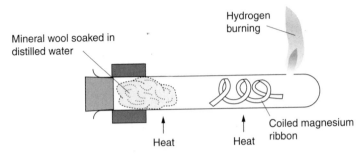

Figure 11.1 Magnesium reacting with steam.

2. Heat the metal until it starts to glow, then heat the mineral wool to produce steam.

3. Move the Bunsen burner backwards and forwards between the mineral wool and the metal powder and, when the hot metal begins to react with the steam, ignite the gas escaping.

4. Continue heating the mineral wool until the reaction subsides.

5. Repeat the procedure for each metal.

Sample results

Metal	Observation
Magnesium	Large yellow flame, white residue left, black crystalline appearance of the glass under the magnesium ribbon.
Zinc	Small yellow flame, yellow residue which turned white on cooling.
Iron	No flame, iron slightly black on the edge of the sample.

Notes

1. The results show a reactivity order of:

   $Mg > Zn > Fe$

2. The gas escaping was hydrogen.

3. The residues were the metal oxides.

4. The black crystalline appearance of the glass under the magnesium was silicon from the glass.

5. Equations for the reactions:

$$Mg + H_2O \rightarrow MgO + H_2$$

$$2Mg + SiO_2 \rightarrow 2MgO + Si$$

$$Zn + H_2O \rightarrow ZnO + H_2$$

$$Fe + H_2O \rightarrow FeO + H_2$$

11.5 Comparing the reactivity of halogens by studying their displacement by one another

Chlorine water ($0.5\,mol\,dm^{-3}$)
Bromine water ($0.5\,mol\,dm^{-3}$)
Iodine-potassium iodide solution
(dissolve 20 g of potassium iodide
and 12.7 g of iodine in $200\,cm^3$ of
distilled water and dilute to $1\,dm^3$)
Potassium chloride solution
($1\,mol\,dm^{-3}$)
Potassium bromide solution
($1\,mol\,dm^{-3}$)

Potassium iodide solution
($1\,mol\,dm^{-3}$)
Cyclohexane
Six test-tubes with corks in a rack
Measuring cylinder ($10\,cm^3$)
Eye protection
Access to fume cupboard

Safety Chlorine water and bromine water are both toxic and corrosive so they should be used in a fume cupboard. Cyclohexane is highly flammable and harmful. Eye protection is essential.

Method

1. In test-tubes, mix $2\,cm^3$ of a halogen solution with $2\,cm^3$ of a solution containing halide ions.

2. Add $2\,cm^3$ of cyclohexane, cork the tube and shake it vigorously.

3. When layers have separated, note the appearance of the organic layer.

4. Carry out the procedure with different halogen and halide ion combinations.

Sample results

| | | Halide ions | |
Halogen	Chloride	Bromide	Iodide
Chlorine	–	organic layer brown	organic layer purple
Bromine	no reaction	–	organic layer purple
Iodine	no reaction	no reaction	–

Notes

1. Produce chlorine water by bubbling chlorine through distilled water, in a fume cupboard.

2. Halogens are soluble in non-polar organic solvents whereas halide ions are not. Separating the halogens from the halide ions by solvent extraction with cyclohexane makes their identification easier.

3. The results show that chlorine displaced bromine and iodine, and bromine displaced iodine, giving a reactivity order of:

   $Cl_2 > Br_2 > I_2$

4. The halide ion being displaced becomes oxidised by transferring an electron to the halogen displacing it:

   $Cl_2 + 2Br^- \rightarrow Br_2 + 2Cl^-$

   $Cl_2 + 2I^- \rightarrow I_2 + 2Cl^-$

   $Br_2 + 2I^- \rightarrow I_2 + 2Br^-$

5. The smaller the atom, the more readily the electron is accepted for the same reason given in 11.3, note 3. Therefore reactivity decreases on descending group 7 of the Periodic Table.

6. Do not use rubber bungs because cyclohexane reacts with rubber.

11.6 The pulsating heart demonstration

Watch glass
Mercury
Iron nail (5 cm)
Potassium manganate(VII)
Forceps
Latex gloves

Distilled water
Concentrated sulfuric(VI) acid
Teat pipette (dropper)
Overhead projector
Eye protection

Safety Concentrated sulfuric(VI) acid is corrosive. Potassium manganate(VII) is harmful and a powerful oxidising agent. Great care must be taken to prevent concentrated sulfuric(VI) acid coming into contact with potassium manganate(VII) crystals except in the context of this demonstration. Dangerous explosions can occur.

Mercury vapour is toxic but the risk is low by inhalation if the mercury is kept under water. Mercury attacks gold, silver and aluminium. Eye protection is essential. Wear latex gloves when handling mercury and wash hands thoroughly afterwards. Work in a clear plastic tray in order to contain any mercury spillage.

Method

1. Put the watch glass on the overhead projector.
2. Put a globule of mercury on the watch glass and cover it with distilled water.
3. Add one drop of concentrated sulfuric(VI) acid.
4. Using forceps add two crystals of potassium manganate(VII).
5. Place the nail in the mixture so that the point just touches the mercury.
6. Switch on the overhead projector so that the audience can view the image on the screen.

Sample results

The globule of mercury begins to pulsate like a beating heart.

Notes

1. The nail must be new and free from grease or corrosion. Propanone will remove any grease.
2. The movement of the globule of mercury is a charge–discharge phenomenon:

$$Mn^{7+} + 5e^- \rightarrow Mn^{2+}$$

$$Hg^0 - 2e^- \rightarrow Hg^{2+}$$

11.7 Studying the corrosion of iron using ferroxyl indicator

Glass Petri dish

Iron nail (5 cm)

Top-pan balance

Sodium chloride

Potassium hexacyanoferrate(III)

Phenolphthalein solution (1%)

Safety Phenolphthalein is a purgative and in a highly flammable solvent.

Method

1. Prepare the ferroxyl indicator by dissolving 20 g of sodium chloride and 2 g of potassium hexacyanoferrate(III) in 200 cm^3 of distilled water. Add 2 cm^3 of phenolphthalein solution and dilute to 1dm^3 with distilled water.

2. Fill the Petri dish with the ferroxyl solution and totally immerse the nail in the ferroxyl solution.

Sample results

After about 15 minutes the solution at each end of the nail turns blue and the solution around the rest of the nail is red.

Notes

1. The blue colour is caused by oxidised iron reacting with the potassium hexacyanoferrate(III):

2. $Fe^0 - 2e^- \rightarrow Fe^{2+}$

   $Fe^{2+} + [Fe^{III}(CN)_6]^{3-} \rightarrow Fe^{3+} + [Fe^{II}(CN)_6]^{4-}$

   $K^+ + Fe^{3+} + [Fe^{II}(CN)_6]^{4-} \rightarrow KFe^{III}[Fe^{II}(CN)_6]$

3. The red colour is the result of oxygen from air and water accepting the electrons lost by the iron, to produce hydroxide ions which turn phenolphthalein red.

   $O_2 + 2H_2O + 2e^- \rightarrow 4OH^-$

11.8 To show that carbon monoxide is a reducing agent

Test-tube fitted with a bung and 10 cm of straight glass tubing

Zinc oxide

Powdered carbon

Copper(II) oxide

Retort stand and clamp

Two Bunsen burners

Chattaway spatula with a circular cross section shank (flat part of the handle cut off)

Eye protection

Safety Copper compounds are harmful. Eye protection essential.

Method

1. Put three large rounded spatula measures of zinc oxide into the test-tube.

2. Add four large rounded spatula measures of powdered carbon.

3. Close the tube with a bung and shake the test-tube to mix the contents.

4. Immerse the glass tube into the copper(II) oxide, remove it and use the shank of the spatula to push the copper(II) oxide into the tube.

5. Fit the bung and glass tube containing the copper(II) oxide to the test-tube containing the zinc oxide-carbon mixture.

6. Hold the test-tube horizontally in the clamp and stand (see Figure 11.2).

7. Heat the mixture in the test-tube with one Bunsen burner and then heat the copper(II) oxide in the glass tube with the other Bunsen burner.

8. Observe any change in the appearance of the copper(II) oxide.

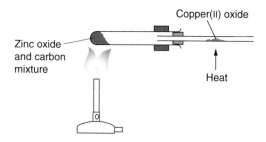

Figure 11.2 Carbon monoxide as a reducing agent.

Sample results

The copper(II) oxide changed colour from black to brown.

Notes

1. Zinc oxide and carbon, when heated, react together to produce carbon monoxide:

$$ZnO + C \rightarrow Zn + CO$$

2. The carbon monoxide reduces the copper(II) oxide to metallic copper:

$$CuO + CO \rightarrow Cu + CO_2$$

3. If the glass tube containing the copper(II) oxide is heated too strongly it will bend, so you may have to straighten it out again by lifting the end of the tube with the spatula.

11.9 Oxidation states of vanadium

Ammonium polytrioxovanadate (metavanadate) (NH_4VO_3)
Zinc powder
Sulfuric(VI) acid ($1\,mol\,dm^{-3}$)
Spatula

Boiling tube
Distilled water
Bunsen burner
Eye protection

Safety $1\,mol\,dm^{-3}$ **sulfuric(VI) acid is irritant. Zinc powder is flammable and can be a fire hazard. Ammonium polytrioxovanadate is toxic (solid and solution ≥ 0.08 M). Eye protection is essential.**

Method

1. Add one spatula measure of ammonium polytrioxovanadate to the boiling tube and add about $5\,cm^3$ of distilled water. Heat over a Bunsen burner flame to dissolve.

2. Add $5\,cm^3$ of sulfuric(VI) acid followed by a spatula measure of zinc powder.

3. Observe the colour changes that take place over a period of 30 minutes with intermittent swirling.

Sample results

The colour of the solution changes from yellow to green, to blue, to green, and lastly purple.

Notes

1. A transition element is one that has a partly filled d-subshell which gives rise to more than one oxidation state.

2. The different colours correspond to the different oxidation states of vanadium:

Colour	Oxidation state	Electron configuration
Yellow	+5	d^2
Green	Mixture of +5 and +4	d^2 and d^3
Blue	+4	d^3
Green	+3	d^4
Purple	+2	d^5

3. The zinc powder is a reducing agent which reduces the vanadium through all available oxidation states.

4. This is a simple and quick experiment to demonstrate the variable oxidation states of a transition metal.

11.10 To demonstrate that the colour of transition metal compounds is the result of partially filled d-orbitals

Sodium thiosulfate solution ($40\,g/dm^3$)   Test-tube
Copper(II) sulfate(VI) solution
    ($0.5\,mol\,dm^{-3}$)

Safety Low hazard.

Method

Mix equal quantities of copper(II) sulfate(VI) and sodium thiosulfate solutions and observe the colour change.

Sample result

The blue copper(II) sulfate(VI) solution becomes colourless.

Notes

1. Cu(II) (d^9) ion is blue. Thiosulfate reduces it to Cu(I)(d^{10}) which is colourless.

2. Cu(I) compounds are white solids. The thiosulfate complexes with the copper(I) to make it soluble.

3. Compounds of transition elements with electron configurations of d^0 and d^{10} are colourless because photons have insufficient energy to stabilise electron transitions.

11.11 Colour changes associated with ligand substitution in transition element compounds

Anhydrous copper(II) sulfate(VI)
Ammonia solution (s.g. 0.88)
Concentrated hydrochloric acid
Distilled water

Spatula
Test-tubes
Measuring cylinder ($10\,cm^3$)
Eye protection

Safety Anhydrous copper(II) sulfate(VI) is harmful. Hydrochloric acid is corrosive. Ammonia solution is corrosive. The vapour is toxic and can cause asthma attacks in susceptible people. Hydrochloric acid and ammonia solution should be handled in a fume cupboard.

Method

1. Using the spatula, transfer the anhydrous copper(II) sulfate(VI) (enough to cover a finger nail) to a test-tube.

2. Add in succession, $3\,cm^3$ of distilled water, and $3\,cm^3$ of hydrochloric acid, $3\,cm^3$ of distilled water and $3\,cm^3$ of ammonia solution and note the colour changes that occur.

Sample results

Effect on colour of adding the various ligands to aqueous copper(II) sulfate(VI) solution:

Distilled water : Pale blue

Hydrochloric acid : Green

Ammonia solution : Deep blue

Notes

1. A ligand is an atom or group of atoms or ions which are capable of forming dative covalent bonds with a transition element. Ligands possess lone pairs of electrons which enable them to do this.

2. During the formation of complex ions, the electrons in the d-orbitals of the transition element which are closest to the ligand are repelled by the ligand's electrons so that the energy of such orbitals will be raised relative to the others. This results in a splitting of the d-subshell (see Figure 11.3)

   e.g. Cu^{2+}: d^9

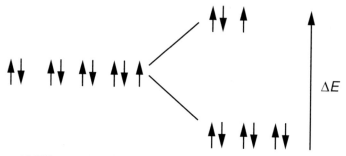

Figure 11.3 The energy difference is given by Planck's equation: $\Delta E = hf$, where h = Planck constant and f = frequency of electromagnetic radiation.

3. Radiation of the frequency given by Planck's equation will raise an electron from the lower 3d to the upper 3d of transition elements and this radiation is part of the visible spectrum. Hydrated copper(II) ions are blue because red light of the appropriate frequency is absorbed and the remainder reflected:

   White – red = blue

4. There are varying degrees of stability which depend on the degree to which different ligands split the d-subshell, i.e. their polarising power. Stability decreases with decreased absorption of red light.

5. A more stabilising ligand will displace a lesser one from its complex. The order of stability of the complexes formed was:

   $[Cu(NH_3)_4]^{2+} > [Cu(H_2O)_6]^{2+} > [CuCl_4]^{2-}$

11.12 Ligand substitution of iron(III) thiocyanate

Iron(III) chloride solution
(1 mol dm⁻³)
Potassium thiocyanate solution
(1 mol dm⁻³)
Sodium fluoride solution (1 mol dm⁻³)
Aluminium sulfate(VI) solution
(1 mol dm⁻³)

Beaker (100 cm³)
Glass rod
Measuring cylinders
(10 cm³ and 100 cm³)
Eye protection

Safety 1 mol dm⁻³ iron(III) chloride is irritant. 1 mol dm⁻³ sodium fluoride is toxic.

Method

1. Mix 5 cm^3 of iron(III) chloride and potassium thiocyanate solutions, stir with the glass rod and observe the colour change.

2. Slowly add sodium fluoride solution from the 100 cm^3 measuring cylinder with stirring until the mixture changes colour from red to white. This should require about 35 cm^3 of sodium fluoride solution.

3. Slowly add 30 cm^3 of aluminium sulfate(VI) solution whilst stirring with the glass rod and observe the colour change.

Results

Adding potassium thiocyanate to iron(III) chloride produced a blood-red colour. Adding fluoride ions to this gradually turned the solution colourless. Adding aluminium ions restored the blood-red colour.

Notes

1. Thiocyanate ions act as ligands to form the $[Fe(CNS)]^{2+}$ ion with Fe(III) which is blood-red.

2. Fluoride ions are more polarising than thiocyanate and therefore displace the thiocyanate from the complex. The destruction of the iron(III) thiocyanate complex by fluoride ions renders the solution colourless.

3. Aluminium ions have a greater affinity for fluoride ions than do iron(III) ions and so the iron(III) ions become free to re-complex with the thiocyanate and so the blood-red colour is restored.

4. This experiment can be extended as an A-level assignment to develop a quantitative method of analysis for aluminium in drinking water. Titrate drinking water with fluoride ions using iron(III) thiocyanate as an indicator. The indicator changes from red to colourless at the end point because aluminium ions react with the added fluoride until the aluminium is exhausted, and then further addition of fluoride ions destroys the iron(III) thiocyanate complex.

12 REACTIVITY OF METALS AND EXTRACTION METHODS

Most metals exist as compounds or ores in the rocks which make up the Earth's crust. Metals can be put into three main groups according to their tendency to become oxidised. Highly reactive metals such as sodium and potassium occur mainly as the chloride in sea water and underground brines. Those of moderate reactivity such as iron and tin occur in rocks as the oxide, sulfide or carbonate and the unreactive metals such as gold occur native, i.e. in the uncombined state. The boundaries between these groups are not sharply defined, e.g. calcium is a fairly reactive metal which occurs mainly as the carbonate whereas mercury is fairly unreactive and occurs as the sulfide ore. However, this classification is acceptable when studying the methods of extraction of the metals from their ores. Metals from the first group are usually extracted by electrolysis of the molten ore or from brine using a mercury cathode. Metals of the second group are extracted by reducing the ore with carbon. The third group of metals can be extracted by just heating the ore in air.

12.1 Heating mercury(II) oxide

Test-tubes, one fitted with a bung and
     double-bend delivery tube
Retort stand and clamp
Ice-cream tub
Spoon spatula

Mercury(II) oxide
Wooden splint
Bunsen burner
Eye protection

Safety Mercury compounds are very toxic. Mercury metal attacks silver and gold so remove hand jewellery. This experiment must be done in a fume cupboard. Dispose of the mercury condensate in a mercury waste bottle. Remove the delivery tube from the water before taking the Bunsen burner away, otherwise there is the danger of cold water being sucked into the hot test-tube as it cools.

Method

1. Assemble the apparatus as shown in Figure 12.1.

2. Put one rounded spatula measure of mercury oxide in the test-tube and heat the test-tube with the Bunsen burner.

3. Note the appearance of the condensate at the top of the tube.

4. Test the gas with a glowing splint.

Sample results

Globules of mercury condensed at the top of the tube and the gas rekindled a glowing splint showing that it was oxygen.

Notes

1. The equation for the reaction:

   $$2HgO \rightarrow 2Hg + O_2$$

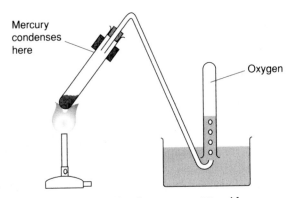

Figure 12.1 Heating mercury(II) oxide.

12.2 Reducing a metal oxide with carbon

Three porcelain crucibles   Bunsen burner
Spoon spatula   Tripod
Iron(III) oxide   Pipe-clay triangle
Copper(II) oxide   Powdered charcoal
Lead(II) oxide (PbO)   Eye protection
Bar magnet   Access to fume cupboard

Safety Lead(II) oxide is toxic. The effects are cumulative. Pregnant women or younger pupils should not handle these substances. There is the danger of damage to the unborn child. The experiment using lead(II) oxide should be carried out in a fume cupboard.

Method

1. Mix each ore in turn with an equal quantity of charcoal in a crucible.

2. Put the crucible on a pipe-clay triangle on a tripod and heat strongly with the Bunsen burner.

3. Test the mixture containing iron(III) oxide with the magnet before and after heating.

Sample results

Ore	Effect of heating with charcoal
Iron(III) oxide	Mixture became magnetic
Lead(II) oxide	Globules of molten lead formed
Copper(II) oxide	Brown tinges of copper formed

Note

The equations for the reactions:

$$2Fe_2O_3 + 3C \rightarrow 4Fe + 3CO_2$$

$$2PbO + C \rightarrow 2Pb + CO_2$$

$$2CuO + C \rightarrow 2Cu + CO_2$$

12.3 Electrolysis of brine using a mercury cathode

Apparatus/reagents as in Figure 12.4, plus plastic ice-cream tub and access to fume cupboard.

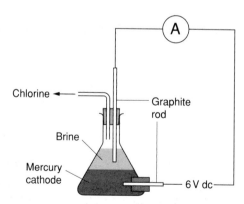

Figure 12.4 Kelner–Solvay cell for the electrolysis of brine.

Safety The electrolysis should be carried out in a fume cupboard because of the production of chlorine which is toxic and irritant. Mercury vapour is toxic, but there should be no risk from inhaling mercury vapour because the mercury is under water. Stand the

Kelner-Solvay cell in a plastic ice-cream tub to catch the mercury in the event of a breakage.

Method

1. Carry out the electrolysis for 15 minutes.

2. Test the gas escaping from the glass tube with damp blue litmus paper.

3. Decant off the brine from the mercury.

4. Add some distilled water to the mercury and swirl the flask.

5. Test the supernatant with red litmus paper.

Sample results

The gas produced at the anode bleached litmus. Bubbles of gas formed in the mercury when the flask was swirled. The supernatant turned red litmus blue.

Notes

1. A sodium–mercury amalgam was produced by the electrolysis. The equations for the reactions occurring at each electrode:

   Cathode: $Na^+ + e^- \rightarrow Na^0$

   Anode: $2Cl^- - 2e^- \rightarrow Cl_2$

2. The bubbles of gas which formed in the mercury were hydrogen and the reaction of the supernatant to litmus was caused by sodium hydroxide, both of which were formed by the sodium in the amalgam reacting with water:

   $2Na + 2H_2O \rightarrow 2NaOH + H_2$

3. Flasks can be obtained from Griffin Education, cat. no: EKW-224-538S.

13 REACTION KINETICS

Chemical reactions take place when the reacting particles collide with each other with sufficient kinetic energy to react. This energy is called the activation energy for the reaction. The colliding particles also have to be correctly oriented with respect to each other for the collision to be fruitful. Any factor which enhances these factors will increase the rate of reaction.

Catalysts are substances which increase the rate of chemical reactions but remain chemically unchanged at the end. They do this by interacting with the particles to orientate them correctly and thus lower the activation energy for the reaction. Increasing the concentration of the reacting particles increases the rate of reaction by increasing the frequency of the collisions. Catalysts also work by this mechanism because the concentration of the reacting particles increases at the catalyst surface.

Increasing the temperature provides more particles with more kinetic energy and increasing the surface area of the reacting substances exposes more particles to the attacking reagent. So, the rate of reaction can be increased by increasing concentration, increasing temperature, increasing the surface area and by using catalysts.

13.1 Qualitative illustration of rate of reaction

Overhead projector
Petri dish
Distilled water
Calcium

Spatula
Teat pipette (dropper)
Hydrochloric acid ($2\,mol\,dm^{-3}$)
Eye protection

Safety $2\,mol\,dm^{-3}$ **hydrochloric acid is irritant. Calcium is highly flammable. Eye protection essential.**

Method

1. Place the Petri dish on the overhead projector. Half fill the Petri dish with distilled water.

2. Add a few granules of calcium and observe the projected image.

3. Using the pipette, add a few drops of dilute hydrochloric acid and observe the change in the projected image.

Sample result

Bubbles of gas are produced soon after the calcium is added to the water in the Petri dish. Adding dilute hydrochloric acid increases the rate of gas formation.

Notes

1. This activity provides a very good introduction to reaction kinetics.

2. Water partially ionises to produce oxonium ions according to the following equation:

$$2H_2O \rightarrow H_3O^+ + OH^-$$

Calcium reacts with oxonium ions to produce hydrogen according to the following equation:

$$Ca + 2H_3O^+ \rightarrow Ca^{2+} + H_2 + 2H_2O$$

3. When the hydrochloric acid is introduced it increases the concentration of oxonium ions which increases the rate of reaction.

$$HCl + H_2O \rightarrow H_3O^+ + Cl^-$$

13.2 Catalytic decomposition of hydrogen peroxide

Spoon spatula
Plastic forceps
Hydrogen peroxide (2.5 vol)
Measuring cylinders (25 cm^3)
Conical flask (250 cm^3) fitted with a
    bung and flexible delivery tube
Ice-cream tub

Retort stand and clamp
Test-tubes
Stop-watch
Test-tubes (100 × 16 mm)
Wooden splints
Eye protection

Safety Risks are low with hydrogen peroxide at concentrations less than 18 vol.

Method

Set up the apparatus as shown in Figure 13.1 for use in subsequent experiments.

Note

Hydrogen peroxide decomposes to form water and oxygen according to the following equation:

$$2H_2O_2 \xrightarrow{\text{catalyst}} 2H_2O + O_2$$

Measuring the rate of evolution of oxygen provides a method of studying the rate of this reaction.

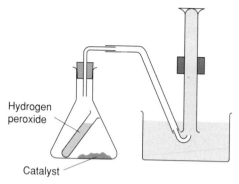

Figure 13.1 Catalytic decomposition of hydrogen peroxide.

13.2.1 Which of a range of compounds is the best catalyst?

Additional apparatus/reagents as follows:
Oxides of zinc, iron, manganese, magnesium, aluminium, lead and copper
Eye protection

Safety Copper(II) oxide and manganese(IV) oxide are both harmful. Lead(IV) oxide is toxic. The effects are cumulative. Pregnant women or younger pupils should not handle this substance. There is the danger of damage to the unborn child.

Method

1. Set up the apparatus as shown in Figure 13.1.

2. Measure out one level spatula-measure of the compound (approximately 0.5 g) to be tested and transfer it to the conical flask.

3. Using a measuring cylinder, measure out 10 cm³ of hydrogen peroxide and transfer it to the test-tube. The test-tube should be full.

4. Using plastic forceps, place the test-tube of hydrogen peroxide into the conical flask taking care not to spill any onto the catalyst, and fit the bung and delivery tube.

5. Mix the contents of the conical flask and measure the volume of gas produced after one minute.

6. Show that the gas produced is oxygen by using it to rekindle a glowing splint.

7. Repeat the procedure for each compound and display the results in the form of a bar chart.

8. The compound which gives the biggest volume of gas in one minute is the most effective catalyst.

Sample results

Compound	Vol/cm^3 of gas produced
Zinc oxide	0
Copper(II) oxide	0.5
Aluminium oxide	0
Manganese(IV) oxide	23.0
Iron(III) oxide	0
Magnesium oxide	0
Lead(IV) oxide	25.0

Notes

1. The volume of oxygen produced from $10\,cm^3$ of $2.5\,vol\ H_2O_2 = 25\,cm^3$.

2. A $25\,cm^3$ gas syringe could be used as an alternative to the measuring cylinder for collecting the gas.

3. Fitting rubber sleeves on the end of the forceps will provide more grip on the test-tube.

4. The glass tube at the end of the rubber delivery tube needs to have been drawn out into a fine capillary tube so that the gas comes out in small bubbles. It should also be hook shaped to fit under the inverted measuring cylinder.

13.2.2 Effect of increasing concentration of hydrogen peroxide

Additional apparatus/reagents as follows:
Manganese(IV) oxide

Hydrogen peroxide, 2.5, 5.0, 7.5, 10.0, 12.5 vol
Eye protection

Safety Manganese(IV) oxide is harmful.

Method

1. Use the same procedure as outlined in 13.2.1 but using 2.5, 5.0, 7.5, 10.0 and 12.5 vol. hydrogen peroxide and measure the time required for $20\,cm^3$ of gas to be produced.

2. Plot a line graph of concentration of hydrogen peroxide on the x-axis and time on the y-axis.

Sample results

Conc. of H_2O_2/vol	Time for $20\,cm^3$ of gas produced/s
2.5	18.00
5.0	6.03
7.5	3.72
10.0	3.20
12.5	3.07

Notes

1. Increasing the concentration of hydrogen peroxide increases the rate of reaction because more particles come into contact with the catalyst quicker.

2. More able students should plot rate in terms of cm^3/s against concentration.

13.2.3 Effect of increasing temperature of hydrogen peroxide

Additional apparatus/reagents as follows:

Thermometer $(0 - 100\,°C)$

Bunsen burner, tripod and gauze
Manganese(IV) oxide
Eye protection

Safety Manganese(IV) oxide is harmful.

Method

1. Use the same procedure as outlined in 13.2.1 and repeat at different temperatures.

2. Use the Bunsen burner to heat 2.5 vol hydrogen peroxide and then, using a measuring cylinder, transfer $10\,cm^3$ to the test-tube.

3. Measure the temperature before and after the reaction has finished and use the average as the temperature at which the reaction took place.

4. Plot a line graph of temperature on the x-axis and time for 20 cm^3 of gas to be produced, on the y-axis.

Results

Initial temp/°C	Final temp/°C	Average temp/°C	Time for 20 cm^3 of gas to be formed/s
10	15	12.5	19.20
19	19	19.0	14.88
31	26	28.5	11.59
40	33	36.5	5.03
48	35	41.5	3.38

Notes

1. Increasing the temperature gives the particles more kinetic energy so they move quicker and therefore come into contact with the catalyst quicker, so the rate of reaction increases.

2. Use an ice bath to regulate temperatures below room temperature.

3. Hydrogen peroxide begins to decompose fairly rapidly at temperatures above 50 °C without the catalyst so do not exceed this temperature.

4. More able students should plot rate in terms of cm^3 s^{-1} against temperature.

13.2.4 Effect of increasing surface area of catalyst

Additional apparatus/reagents as follows:
White glazed ceramic tile
Scalpel
Mortar and pestle

Silver sand
Top-pan balance
Watch glass
Liver (lamb or pig)
Eye protection

Safety Make sure you handle and dispose of the liver hygienically and use disinfectant to wash up equipment after use.

Method

1. Add 3 g of silver sand to 3 g of liver in a mortar, and grind it to a paste with the pestle.

2. Using a scalpel, cut up another liver sample into half centimetre cubes.

3. Leave the other liver sample intact.

4. Using 1 g samples of whole and chopped liver (about the size of a 1 p coin) and 2 g of the sand-liver paste to allow for the sand in the sample, carry out the procedure outlined in 13.2.1 using each liver sample in turn with 10 cm^3 of 2.5 vol hydrogen peroxide.

5. Display the results as a bar chart.

Sample results

Liver sample	Time for 20 cm^3 of gas to be produced/s
Whole	10.81
Diced	7.80
Paste	1.75

Notes

1. Liver contains the enzyme catalase. Catalase is also present in blood, bone marrow, kidney and mucous membranes. Catalase is a haemoprotein which uses one molecule of hydrogen peroxide as a substrate electron donor and another molecule of hydrogen peroxide as an electron acceptor. Hydrogen peroxide is a by-product of mitochondrial and microsomal electron transport systems in cells and is harmful to cells. The destruction of hydrogen peroxide protects membrane lipids and haemoglobin against oxidation by peroxides.

2. Increasing the surface area of the catalyst exposes more of its surface to the hydrogen peroxide particles and thereby increases the rate of reaction.

13.2.5 Effect of increasing mass of catalyst

Additional apparatus/reagents as follows:
Manganese(IV) oxide

Top-pan balance
Eye protection

Safety Manganese(IV) oxide is harmful.

Method

1. Use the procedure outlined in 13.2.1. using 1, 2, 3, 4 and 5 g of manganese(IV) oxide with $10\,cm^3$ of 2.5 vol hydrogen peroxide and measure the time taken to collect $20\,cm^3$ of gas.

2. Plot a line graph of mass of catalyst on the x-axis and time for $20\,cm^3$ of gas to be produced, on the y-axis.

Sample results

Mass/g of catalyst	Time for $20\,cm^3$ of gas to be produced/s
1	13.80
2	9.34
3	5.44
4	4.93
5	4.37

Note

Increasing the mass of catalyst increases the rate of reaction because there is more surface area exposed to the hydrogen peroxide.

13.3 Reaction between sodium thiosulfate and hydrochloric acid

Conical flask ($100\,cm^3$)
Measuring cylinders ($10\,cm^3$ and $50\,cm^3$)
Hydrochloric acid ($2\,mol\,dm^{-3}$)
Sodium thiosulfate ($40\,g/dm^3$)

Felt-tip pen
Scrap paper
Stop watch
Eye protection
Access to fume cupboard

Safety $2\,mol\,dm^{-3}$ **hydrochloric acid is irritant. Toxic sulfur dioxide is produced by the reaction. Do not allow asthmatics to inhale the fumes. The experiment should be carried out in a well ventilated area and the mixtures should be flushed away down the sink in a fume cupboard soon after the measurements have been made.**

Method

1. Using the felt-tip pen, draw a cross on a piece of scrap paper.

2. Using a measuring cylinder, transfer $50\,cm^3$ of sodium thiosulfate solution to a conical flask.

3. Using a 10 cm^3 measuring cylinder, measure out 5 cm^3 of hydrochloric acid.

4. Add the 5 cm^3 of hydrochloric acid to the 50 cm^3 of sodium thiosulfate in the conical flask, swirl the flask to mix, place the flask on the scrap paper over the cross and start the stop watch.

5. View the cross on the scrap paper by looking down from the top of the flask and record the time when the cross just becomes invisible.

Note

This reaction proceeds according to the following equation:

$$Na_2S_2O_3 + 2HCl \rightarrow 2NaCl + SO_2 + H_2O + S$$

The formation of colloidal sulfur turns the mixture opaque and so this provides a method of determining the duration of the reaction, by measuring the time taken for a cross drawn on a piece of paper to become obscured from view by the colloidal sulfur.

13.3.1 Effect of increasing concentration

Additional apparatus/reagents as follows:

Distilled water

Eye protection

Safety 2 mol dm^{-3} **hydrochloric acid is irritant. Toxic sulfur dioxide is produced by the reaction. Do not allow asthmatics to inhale the fumes. The experiment should be carried out in a well ventilated area and the mixtures should be flushed away down the sink in a fume cupboard soon after the measurements have been made.**

Method

1. Carry out the procedure given in 13.3 using these dilutions for the sodium thiosulfate:

Dilution	Sodium thiosulfate/cm^3	Water/cm^3
0.2	10	40
0.4	20	30
0.6	30	20
0.8	40	10
1.0	50	0

2. Plot a line graph of dilution on the x-axis and time for the cross to become invisible on the y-axis.

Sample results

Dilution	Time/s
0.2	96
0.4	48
0.6	25
0.8	13
1.0	6

Notes

1. Diluting the sodium thiosulfate decreases the rate of reaction because there are less frequent collisions between reacting particles due to fewer particles being present.

2. More able students should plot molar concentration against rate (1/temperature), a dilution of 1.0 being $0.25 \, mol \, dm^{-3}$.

3. A-level students could find the reaction order by plotting three graphs: Rate against concentration, rate against 1/concentration and rate against $\log_{10}$ concentration. The graph which produces a straight line shows the reaction order, i.e. 0, 1 or 2 respectively.

13.3.2 Effect of increasing temperature

Additional apparatus/reagents as follows:

Thermometer (0–100 °C)
Bunsen burner

Tripod and gauze
Distilled water
Eye protection

Safety 2 mol dm^{-3} hydrochloric acid is irritant. Toxic sulfur dioxide is produced by the reaction. Do not allow asthmatics to inhale the fumes. The experiment should be carried out in a well ventilated area and the mixtures should be flushed away down the sink in a fume cupboard soon after the measurements have been made. Use chilled sodium thiosulfate to reduce the risk of producing sulfur dioxide.

Method

1. Follow the procedure given in 13.3 using $50 \, cm^3$ of 0.2 dilution of chilled sodium thiosulfate and repeat for a range of temperatures between 0 and 30 °C.

2. Stand the flask containing the sodium thiosulfate on the tripod and

gauze and, using the Bunsen, heat it to 5 °C above the required temperature.

3. Add 5 cm^3 of hydrochloric acid, swirl the flask to mix and stand it over the cross on the scrap paper, start the stop watch and measure the temperature.

4. Record the time for the cross to become invisible and measure the temperature again. Use the average temperature as the temperature at which the reaction took place.

5. Plot a line graph of temperature on the x-axis and time on the y-axis.

Sample results

Temperature/°C			
Initial	Final	Average	Time/s
20	20	20	190
25	25	25	128
34	35	34	77
42	40	41	59
55	54	55	28

Notes

1. Increasing the temperature increases the rate of reaction because of more frequent fruitful collisions between reacting particles due to the particles having more kinetic energy at higher temperatures.

2. More able students should plot temperature against 1/time.

3. For A-level, a plot of $\log_e(1/\text{temperature})$ against 1/time should give a straight line of gradient E_A/R from which the activation energy for the reaction can be calculated (Arrhenius equation). From the above data $E_A/R = 55.8$ and $E_A = 6.71$ kJ/mole (using $R = 8.31$ J mol^{-1} K^{-1}).

13.4 Reaction between hydrochloric acid and marble chips

Top-pan balance capable of weighing to two decimal places
Conical flask (100 cm^3)
Forceps
Scrap paper

Hydrochloric acid (2 mol dm^{-3})
Marble chips
Measuring cylinder (25 cm^3)
Stop watch
Eye protection

Safety $2\,mol\,dm^{-3}$ hydrochloric acid is irritant. Fit a loose plug of cotton wool in the neck of the flask to prevent a fine spray of acid as the reaction mixture effervesces.

Method

1. Weigh out 2.5 g of marble chips onto a piece of scrap paper using the forceps to pick out the chips.

2. Using the measuring cylinder, transfer 25 cm³ of hydrochloric acid to a conical flask and loosely plug the neck of the flask with cotton wool.

3. Place the conical flask containing the acid onto the pan of the balance.

4. Remove the cotton-wool plug. Simultaneously, add the marble chips to the acid and start the stop watch and replace the cotton-wool plug.

5. Record the mass every 30 s for 5 minutes (10 readings). The starting mass will be the mass of the beaker + acid + 2.5 g of marble chips.

6. Draw a line graph of time on the x-axis and loss in mass on the y-axis. The slope of the line gives a measure of the rate of reaction.

Notes

1. Marble is a metamorphic rock composed of calcium carbonate. Hydrochloric acid reacts with calcium carbonate to form calcium chloride, water and carbon dioxide. The equation is:

$$CaCO_3 + 2HCl \rightarrow CaCl_2 + H_2O + CO_2$$

The rate at which carbon dioxide is produced provides a method of measuring the rate of reaction. The most convenient way of doing this is by following the loss in mass as the gas is evolved, because carbon dioxide is sufficiently dense to cause measurable decreases in mass using a standard laboratory balance.

2. You could carry out a preliminary experiment by adding hydrochloric acid to some marble chips and show that the gas evolved is carbon dioxide by its reaction with limewater. Carry out the reaction in a test-tube and hold a piece of glass tubing previously dipped in limewater in the top of the test-tube. The limewater globule in the end of the glass tubing turns milky.

13.4.1 Effect of increasing the concentration of hydrochloric acid

Additional apparatus/reagents as follows:
An extra measuring cylinder (25 cm³)

Distilled water
Eye protection

Safety 2 mol dm⁻³ hydrochloric acid is irritant. Fit a loose plug of cotton wool in the neck of the flask to prevent a fine spray of acid as the reaction mixture effervesces.

Method

1. Carry out the procedure given in 13.4 using different concentrations of hydrochloric acid diluted with distilled water, as follows:

Molar concentration	Vol of acid/cm³	Vol of water/cm³
0.4	5	20
0.8	10	15
1.2	15	10
1.6	20	5
2.0	25	0

2. Plot line graphs of loss in mass against time for each concentration of hydrochloric acid and find the gradient of each of the graphs. This gives the rate of reaction for each concentration.

3. Plot a line graph of rate against concentration.

Sample results

	Mass/g at different concentrations/mol dm⁻³				
Time/s	0.4	0.8	1.2	1.6	2.0
0	76.64	77.22	77.20	77.07	76.72
30	76.64	77.22	77.20	77.07	76.71
60	76.64	77.21	77.19	77.06	76.69
90	76.63	77.21	77.18	77.05	76.67
120	76.63	77.20	77.18	77.05	76.65
150	76.62	77.20	77.17	77.03	76.63
180	76.62	77.19	77.16	77.02	76.61
210	76.62	77.19	77.15	77.01	76.59
240	76.61	77.19	77.14	77.00	76.57
270	76.61	77.18	77.13	76.98	76.55
300	76.61	77.17	77.12	76.97	76.53
Total loss in mass	0.03	0.05	0.08	0.10	0.19

Notes

1. It is important that you select marble chips of similar size to avoid surface area effects.

2. Increasing the concentration of hydrochloric acid increases the rate of reaction by increasing the number of particles which, in turn, creates more frequent collisions.

3. Less able students could plot the total loss in mass after 5 minutes against dilution; 0.2, 0.4, etc.

4. A-level students could find the reaction order by plotting appropriate graphs.

13.4.2 Effect of temperature

Additional apparatus/reagents as follows:
Thermometer
Bunsen burner
Matches
Tripod and gauze
Eye protection

Safety 2 mol dm⁻³ **hydrochloric acid is irritant. Fit a loose plug of cotton wool in the neck of the flask to prevent a fine spray of acid as the reaction mixture effervesces. Hot hydrochloric acid should be handled with great care because it is corrosive. Have a beaker of sodium carbonate on hand to treat any spillage and mop up immediately using a wet cloth. Use heat resistant gloves when handling the flask containing hot acid.**

Method

1. Carry out the procedure as described in 13.4 and repeat for a range of temperatures.

2. Heat the flask containing the acid to 2 °C above the required temperature and place it onto the pan of the balance.

3. Add the marble chips and record the temperature before and after the readings have been taken.

4. The average of the initial and final temperatures is taken as the temperature at which the reaction took place.

5. Determine the rate of reaction for each temperature by drawing graphs as described in 13.4, and then plot a line graph of temperature on the x-axis and rate on the y-axis.

Sample results

Experiment	Initial temp/°C	Final temp/°C	Average temp/°C
1	20	21	21.5
2	46	38	42.0
3	58	44	51.0
4	67	46	56.5
5	80	49	64.5

Mass for different temperatures/g

Time/s	21.5 °C	42.0 °C	51.0 °C	56.5 °C	64.5 °C
0	77.58	77.15	76.83	76.14	76.52
30	77.54	77.00	76.56	75.81	76.15
60	77.48	76.88	76.36	75.60	75.92
90	77.41	76.78	76.23	75.46	75.76
120	77.35	76.70	76.15	75.37	75.64
150	77.29	76.64	76.10	75.30	75.55
180	77.24	76.60	76.05	75.23	75.48
210	77.19	76.56	76.01	75.17	75.41
240	77.15	76.52	75.98	75.12	75.36
270	77.10	76.49	75.96	75.07	75.30
300	77.07	76.46	75.94	75.03	75.26

Notes

1. You need to be consistent with the size of marble chips to avoid surface area effects.

2. Increasing the temperature increases the rate of reaction because the particles have more kinetic energy thereby participating in more frequent and forceful collisions.

3. Less able students could plot total loss in mass against temperature.

4. A-level students could determine the activation energy for this reaction by plotting rate against $\log_e(1/\text{temperature})$, the gradient of which gives E_A/R (Arrhenius equation) where R = universal gas constant, $8.31 \, \text{J mol}^{-1}\text{K}^{-1}$.

13.4.3 Effect of size of the marble chips

Additional apparatus/reagents as follows:
Mortar and pestle
Eye protection

Safety 2 mol dm^{-3} hydrochloric acid is irritant. Fit a loose plug of cotton wool in the neck of the flask to prevent a fine spray of acid as the reaction mixture effervesces.

Method

1. Wearing eye protection, break up some marble chips using the mortar and pestle and separate them into large, medium and small chips.

2. Carry out the procedure described in 13.4. with 2.5 g of each sample of marble chips and 25 cm^3 of 2 mol dm^{-3} hydrochloric acid.

3. Determine the rate of reaction for each category of chip size as previously described.

Results

Time/s	Mass for different size chips/g		
	Large	Medium	Small
0	72.42	77.67	76.91
30	72.42	77.66	76.90
60	72.42	77.66	76.88
90	72.41	77.65	76.85
120	72.41	77.63	76.82
150	72.40	77.61	76.77
180	72.40	77.60	76.74
210	72.40	77.58	76.72
240	72.39	77.56	76.70
270	72.38	77.54	76.68
300	72.38	77.53	76.66
Total loss in mass	0.04	0.14	0.25

Notes

1. The smaller the size of the marbles chips, the greater the rate of reaction because more surface area of the marble is exposed to the hydrochloric acid.

2. Less able students could plot the total mass lost against chip size.

13.5 Effect of manganese(II) ions on the rate of reaction between potassium manganate(VII) and potassium ethanedioate

Colorimeter fitted with a green filter (see Experiment 5.1)

Potassium manganate(VII) solution ($4.3 \, g/dm^3$)

Manganese(II) sulfate(VI) solution ($6.08 \, g \, MnSO_4.4H_2O/dm^3$)

Acidified potassium ethanedioate (oxalate) solution: Dissolve $1.13 \, g$ of potassium ethanedioate in 800 cm^3 of distilled water and add 50 cm^3 of concentrated H_2SO_4. Dilute to $1 \, dm^3$ with distilled water

Two measuring cylinders (10 and $50 \, cm^3$)

Pipette ($10 \, cm^3$)

Pipette filler

Volumetric flask with stopper ($100 \, cm^3$)

Glass rod

Distilled water

Stop watch

Eye protection

Safety Concentrated sulfuric(VI) acid is corrosive. Potassium ethanedioate is harmful.

Method

1. Using the pipette, pipette filler and volumetric flask, dilute the $4.3 \, g/dm^3$ potassium manganate(VII) solution 1/10.

2. Using the measuring cylinder transfer $5 \, cm^3$ of the diluted potassium manganate(VII) solution to the colorimeter beaker.

3. Add $40 \, cm^3$ of distilled water and mix using the glass rod.

4. Add $5 \, cm^3$ of the potassium ethanedioate solution, stir the mixture with the glass rod and measure the optical density in terms of current/mA every minute for the first 3 minutes, then every 30 s for the next minute and every 10 s thereafter until the ammeter reads 1 mA (full-scale deflection). (See section 5.1.)

5. Plot a line graph of time/s on the x-axis and current/mA on the y-axis.

6. Using the pipette, pipette filler and volumetric flask, dilute the manganese(II) sulfate(VI) solution 1/10 with distilled water.

7. Repeat the procedure with a reaction mixture containing 5 cm^3 of potassium manganate(VII) solution, 5 cm^3 of potassium ethanedioate solution, 35 cm^3 of distilled water and 5 cm^3 of manganese(II) sulfate(VI) solution.

Sample results

	Current/mA	
Time/s	Without MnSO$_4$	With MnSO$_4$
0	0.20	0.20
60	0.21	0.29
120	0.22	0.42
180	0.26	0.72
210	0.30	0.80
240	0.40	0.80
250	0.44	0.80
260	0.48	–
270	0.53	–
280	0.60	–
290	0.70	–
300	0.80	–

Notes

1. This experiment is suitable for a practical assignment at A-level. In acid conditions, ethanedioate ions reduce manganate(VII) ions to manganese(II) ions together with the production of water and carbon dioxide, according to the following equation:

$$2MnO_4^- + 16H^+ + 5C_2O_4^{2-} \rightarrow 2Mn^{2+} + 8H_2O + 10CO_2$$

The reaction mixture gradually changes from purple to colourless as the manganate(VII) is reduced. The reaction proceeds slowly at first and then speeds up. This suggests that the Mn^{2+} ions which are generated by the reaction may be acting as a catalyst.

2. Precipitate the ethanedioate ions with aqueous calcium chloride (1 mol dm^{-3}) before discarding the waste down the sink.

3. More able students could extend this activity by repeating the experiment using a range of manganese concentrations, e.g.:

$MnSO_4/cm^3$	Distilled water/cm^3
5	0
4	1
3	2
2	3
1	4

and/or the already 1/10 diluted solution successively diluted further by factors of 10.

13.6 Factors affecting the rate at which fizzy water goes 'flat'

Three bottles of fizzy water
Plastic bucket
Anti-bumping granules
Spatula
Top-pan balance
Plastic drinks cups or beakers

Measuring cylinder (50 cm^3)
Marker pen
Absorbent paper tissue
Access to a refrigerator and a supply of hot water

Safety Low hazard.

Method

1. Take six similar drinks cups, put 50 cm^3 of tap water in each one and put a graduation mark on each one using a marker pen.

2. Empty each cup and dry it with absorbent paper tissue.

3. Cool one bottle of fizzy water and two plastic drinks cups by placing them in a refrigerator overnight.

4. Warm up another bottle of fizzy water and two drinks cups by standing them in a bucket of hot water prior to the lesson.

5. Keep the other bottle of fizzy water and two cups at room temperature.

6. Add a rounded spatula measure of anti-bumping granules to three of the cups.

7. Remove the bottle of fizzy water from the refrigerator and fill cups with and without anti-bumping granules to the mark with the cold fizzy water.

8. Immediately weigh the cups using the top-pan balance.

9. Repeat the procedure with the bottles of fizzy water stored in hot water and stored at room temperature.

10. Re-weigh the cups of fizzy water after 30 minutes and calculate the loss in mass.

Sample results

Loss in mass/g of $50\,cm^3$ of fizzy water of different temperatures in containers with and without anti-bumping granules after standing for 30 minutes:

	Without anti-bumping granules	With anti-bumping granules
Hot (56 °C)	1.27	1.31
Medium (23 °C)	0.08	0.20
Cold (13.5 °C)	0.06	0.18

Notes

1. This is a simple but effective experiment which could be part of KS1 or KS2 program of study to introduce children to a few of the concepts of reaction kinetics at an early age. Carbon dioxide escaping from fizzy drinks causes the 'fizz'. Bottles of fizzy water are available for a few pence in all supermarkets.

2. Increasing the temperature of the fizzy water increases the escaping tendency of the carbon dioxide particles. Also particles speed up at higher temperatures because they have more kinetic energy so collisions between them will be more forceful, which results in the carbon dioxide particles being 'knocked out' of the solution more readily.

3. Adding anti-bumping granules increases the surface area of the container which provides more nuclei on which bubbles of gas can form.

4. Temperature had a bigger effect than surface area.

13.7 Effect of temperature on the rate of expansion of dough

Live yeast culture
Strong white flour
Cooking salt
Vitamin C (ascorbic acid)
Mixing bowl
Measuring jug (500 cm^3)
Sucrose

Six hypodermic syringes (100 cm^3)
  with septums
Teaspoon
Six beakers (500 cm^3)
Kettle
Ice
Six thermometers

Safety Check that all syringes are returned before the class is dismissed.

Method

Preparation of dough

1. Weigh out 25 g of yeast and 3 g of sucrose into the measuring jug and add a little water. Blend together until creamy and leave it in a warm place to ferment.

2. Weigh out 680 g of flour into the mixing bowl, add a teaspoonful of salt and make a well in the centre of the mixture.

3. Add 300 cm^3 of water to the yeast/sucrose mixture, mix and pour it into the well.

4. Work in the flour from the centre until all the liquid is included, then continue working until the dough comes away from the sides of the bowl.

5. Knead the dough and then work it into a ball adding more water if necessary.

6. Take the dough out of the bowl and place it on a floured surface. Knead the dough until it is of homogeneous consistency.

Effect of temperature on the rising of the dough

1. Pack the syringes with 50 g of dough and cover the ends with the septums.

2. Add 400 cm^3 of water to each of the beakers and produce a range of temperatures using the kettle and ice.

3. Immerse the syringes of dough in the beakers of water and measure the increase in volume after 30 minutes.

4. Measure the temperature of the water in each beaker before and after 30 minutes. Find the average temperature and convert to Kelvin. Calculate the volume change at standard temperature ($273\,K$) by using Charles' law.

5. Plot a line graph of the corrected volume increase/cm^3 on the y-axis and average temperature on the x-axis.

Results

Temperature/°C				Volume/cm^3			
Initial	Final	Average	T/K	Initial	Final	Change	$V_{corrected}$
12	8	10	283	52	59	7	6.8
21	18	20	293	54	70	16	14.9
35	25	30	303	50	73	23	20.7
52	40	46	319	53	80	27	23.1
85	55	70	343	50	71	21	16.7

Notes

1. Enzymes are proteins which act as biological catalysts regulating chemical reactions in living cells. Enzymes are specific in that they are only receptive to one substrate. They operate by a lock and key mechanism in which the substrate particle (the key) fits into an active site in the enzyme (the lock) which is of a complementary shape to the substrate particle. The active site of the enzyme is formed by the way in which the protein folds bringing appropriate functional groups present as side chains into proximity with one another. The activity of enzymes is affected by temperature, pH and metal ions which act as co-factors.

2. Dough is a mixture of ground corn flour, water, yeast and sucrose. The yeast ferments the sucrose in the dough to produce ethanol and carbon dioxide. The carbon dioxide makes the dough rise. Increasing the temperature up to approximately $40\,°C$ increases the rate of fermentation and therefore the rate at which the dough rises. Temperatures above $40\,°C$ will kill the yeast and therefore decrease the rate of fermentation.

3. Yeast contains the enzyme zymase which converts sugar into ethanol and carbon dioxide:

$$\overset{\text{zymase}}{C_6H_{12}O_6 \;\rightarrow\; 2C_2H_5OH + 2CO_2}$$

4. It is necessary to correct the volume change obtained to the volume change at standard temperature because gases expand when hot.

5. The results show that increasing the temperature up to 40 °C increased the rate at which the dough rose because of increased yeast activity.

6. At temperatures above 40 °C, the rate at which the dough rose decreased because of decreased yeast activity.

13.8 Effect of pH on the activity of pepsin in digesting coagulated egg white

Aqueous pepsin solution (2%)	Thermometer
Boiled egg white	Ruler
Cheese grater	Teat pipette (dropper)
Concentrated hydrochloric acid	pH indicator paper
Sodium hydroxide solution ($10 \, mol \, dm^{-3}$)	Three test-tubes
Distilled water	Beakers ($250 \, cm^3$)
Spatula	Measuring cylinder ($10 \, cm^3$)
Top-pan balance	Glass rod
Watch glass	Absorbent paper tissue
Kettle	Stop-watch
	Safety goggles

Safety Concentrated hydrochloric acid is corrosive and 40% sodium hydroxide solution ($10 \, mol \, dm^{-3}$) causes severe burns. Safety goggles (not safety spectacles) must be worn.

Method

1. Using the measuring cylinder, transfer $5 \, cm^3$ of pepsin solution to each of three test-tubes.

2. Using the teat pipette, add three drops of distilled water to the first test-tube, three drops of hydrochloric acid to the second and three drops of sodium hydroxide to the third.

3. Measure the pH of the pepsin solutions by withdrawing a drop using a glass rod and testing it with pH indicator paper. Wash the glass rod under a running tap and wipe dry with absorbent paper tissue between tests.

4. Weigh out three 1 g samples of grated egg white (use the cheese grater) and add to the three test-tubes containing the different pepsin solutions.

5. Place the test-tubes in a beaker of water at 40 °C and maintain this temperature by adding hot water from time to time.

6. Shake the mixtures intermittently.

7. Measure the height of the egg white in the test-tube after 30 minutes.

8. Show the results in the form of a bar chart.

Sample results

pH	Height of egg white after 30 min/cm
Acidic	0.7
Neutral	1.7
Alkaline	2.5

Notes

1. The results show that pepsin is more effective in acid conditions.

2. More able students could measure the height of the egg white every 5 minutes for 30 minutes and plot a graph of decrease in height against time/min. The gradient gives the rate of digestion of the egg white.

3. The experiment could be extended to investigate the effect of temperature and the results should show that the pepsin works quicker at temperatures approaching 40 °C and then becomes less active at temperatures above 40 °C.

13.9 Determination of the Michaelis constant for the action of catalase on hydrogen peroxide

Conical flask (250 cm^3) fitted with a bung and delivery tube
Gas syringe (20 cm^3)
Test-tube (15 × 100 mm)
Fresh liver, the size of a 50 p coin (pig or lamb)
Absorbent paper tissue
Stop-watch
Hydrogen peroxide (10 vol)
Measuring cylinder (10 cm^3)
Distilled water
Eye protection

Safety Dispose of the liver hygienically after use.

Method

1. Set up the apparatus as shown in Figure 13.2.

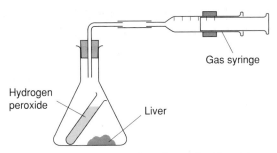

Figure 13.2 Apparatus for measuring the Michaelis constant for the decomposition of hydrogen peroxide by catalase.

2. Mix the contents of the conical flask and measure the time to collect $20\,cm^3$ of gas.

3. Retrieve the liver, rinse it under a cold running tap, blot it dry with absorbent paper tissue to re-use so that re-weighing becomes unnecessary.

4. Repeat the procedure for a range of concentration of hydrogen peroxide, e.g. 2, 4, 6, 8 and 10 vol.

5. Plot a line graph of 1/time on the y-axis and concentration of H_2O_2/vol on the x-axis and extrapolate to find $1/t_{max}$.

6. Use the graph to find the concentration of hydrogen peroxide which corresponds to half $1/t_{max}$. This is the Michaelis constant, K_m.

Results

H_2O_2 conc./vol	Time to collect $20\,cm^3$ of gas/s
2	10.11
4	6.17
6	2.96
8	2.33
10	2.16

V_{max} (in terms of $1/t$) $= 0.17$ so $K_m = 3.7$

Notes

1. See 13.2.4, note 1, for background information about liver enzymes.

2. This activity is suitable for the biochemistry component of A-level chemistry courses.

3. This experiment can be extended by investigating the effect of various metal ions on K_m e.g. Ca, Mg, Fe, Cu, Zn and Hg.

13.10 Comparing the effectiveness of various biological washing powders in dissolving the emulsion on photographic film

Monochrome photographic film (Ilford FP4)

Various brands of biological washing powders

Distilled water

Top-pan balance

Spatula

Measuring cylinder ($10\,cm^3$)

Beaker ($500\,cm^3$)

Thermometer

Ethanoic acid ($2\,mol\,dm^{-3}$)

Scissors

Plastic forceps

Photographic developer made up as: Metol, 2 g; hydroquinone, 5 g; sodium sulfate(IV) (anhydrous), 100 g; borax, 2 g; all in $1\,dm^3$ of distilled water

Photographic fixer made up as: sodium thiosulfate ($300\,g/dm^3$ in distilled water)

Stop-watch

Test-tubes

Kettle

Eye protection

Safety Ethanoic acid is an irritant. Some people will be allergic to enzymes in biological washing powders so avoid skin contact. Hydroquinone is irritant.

Method

1. Expose the photographic film to light by removing it from the cassette.

2. Handle the film with forceps and develop the film by swirling it in a beaker of developer for 7 minutes at room temperature.

3. Transfer the film to another beaker containing ethanoic acid for 1 minute and then into a third beaker of fixer for 2 minutes.

4. Transfer the developed and fixed film to another beaker and wash with 10 changes of water and hang it up to dry.

5. When dry, cut it up into $1 \times 2\,cm$ strips.

6. Dissolve 1 g of washing powder in $5cm^3$ of distilled water and transfer it to a test-tube.

7. Use the kettle to heat some water to between 30 and 40 °C and fill a beaker with the hot water.

8. Place the test-tube containing the washing powder solution in the beaker of hot water and add one strip of the photographic film.

9. Measure the time to the nearest minute for the film to clear.

10. Repeat the procedure for a range of different brands of washing powder.

Sample results

Time/min for film to clear should be in the range 10–20 minutes.

Notes

1. Biological washing powders contain the enzymes known as proteases. Many stains are protein based and proteases in washing powders break down these proteins during washing. Otto Rohm first patented washing powders containing enzymes in 1913. It is important not to wash clothes at too high a temperature when using biological washing powders because temperatures above 40 °C will destroy the enzyme.

2. Photographic film contains a coating of silver iodide dispersed in a gelatin emulsion. When the film is exposed to light, some of the silver iodide is reduced to metallic silver. Developing and fixing removes the unreacted silver iodide leaving metallic silver in the emulsion which appears as a black opaque coating on the film. Gelatin is a protein which is broken down by protease. When this happens the particles of silver no longer stick to the film base and so it becomes transparent.

3. Do not use commercial photographic fixers because they contain aluminium potassium sulphate and boric acid which hardens the emulsion making it less susceptible to attack by the enzyme.

4. The experiment can be extended by investigating temperature and concentration effects on the activity of the enzyme.

13.11 Effect of concentration on protease activity of biological liquid cleaner

Exposed, developed and fixed photographic film (see 13.10)
Ariel biological liquid cleaner
Measuring cylinders (10 cm^3 and 100 cm^3)
Test-tubes

Beaker (250 cm^3)
Marker pen
Distilled water
Kettle of hot water
Thermometer

Safety Some people will be allergic to enzymes in biological cleaner so avoid skin contact.

Method

1. Prepare a 1:100 working solution of biological cleaner by making two successive dilutions of 10 cm^3 of the Ariel liquid to 100 cm^3 with distilled water.

2. Prepare solutions of different concentration of the working biological cleaner in test-tubes as follows:

Tube No.	Vol of working solution/cm^3	Vol of distilled water/cm^3
1	2	8
2	4	6
3	6	4
4	8	2
5	10	0

3. Place the test-tubes in a beaker of water of temperature between 30 and 40 °C.

4. Place one 2 cm × 1 cm piece of film in each test-tube of solution and measure the time to the nearest minute for the film to clear.

5. Plot a line graph of concentration in terms of percentage working solution on the x-axis and time/minute on the y-axis.

Results

Concentration %	Time for film to clear/min
20	20
40	17
60	15
80	11
100	8

Notes

1. The results show that the higher the concentration the quicker the film clears because there is more enzyme to bring about the reaction.

2. More able students should plot rate in terms of 1/t against percentage concentration of the biological liquid.

3. The activity could be extended by investigating the effect of temperature and also pH of biological liquid. The pH can be adjusted by diluting the working solution with standard pH buffer solutions to give a range of pH.

13.12 Factors affecting the rate at which soluble aspirin dissolves

Beaker (100 cm³)
Mortar and pestle
Measuring cylinder (25 cm³)
Stop-watch
Thermometer

Glass rod
Kettle
Distilled water
3 soluble aspirin (or similar) tablets

Safety Supervise the use of aspirin. The students need to handle the hot water with care and adopt responsible behaviour with the tablets.

Method

1. Using the measuring cylinder, transfer 25 cm³ of distilled water to the beaker.

2. Crack an aspirin tablet along its crease and drop it into the beaker of water.

3. Measure the time for the half tablet to dissolve.

4. Repeat the procedure with and without stirring, using crushed and whole half tablets and hot and cold water. Use the kettle to heat the water before measuring out the 25 cm³.

5. Display the results in the form of a bar chart.

Sample results (for Panadol soluble)

Treatment of tablet	Time to dissolve/s	
	Cold	Hot
Whole	127	26
Crushed	32	15

Treatment of mixture	Time to dissolve/s	
	Cold	Hot
Unstirred	102	32
Stirred	56	12

Notes

1. Soluble aspirin are effervescent tablets which dissolve in water. Manufacturers of the tablets claim that drinking already dissolved aspirin alleviates cold and flu symptoms quicker than swallowing an insoluble tablet because the particles of a solution pass more readily into the body. An insoluble tablet has to be digested before the active ingredient can be absorbed. The active ingredient of aspirin tablets is salicylic acid which occurs naturally in willow bark. The old-fashioned remedy for curing headache was to chew a piece of willow bark.

2. Soluble aspirin tablets contain the active ingredient mixed with sodium hydrogencarbonate and citric acid. When the tablets are added to water the citric acid dissolves and reacts with the sodium hydrogencarbonate to produce sodium citrate, water and carbon dioxide (hence the effervescence) and the active ingredient is released into the solution. The quicker the tablets dissolve the quicker they take effect.

3. More able students could extend this activity by carrying out the experiment using a range of temperatures and also comparing whole tablets with broken tablets and powdered tablets.

13.13 Order of reaction

Three measuring cylinders (25 cm^3)
Conical flask (250 cm^3)
White tile
Stop-watch
Burette (50 cm^3)
Sulfuric(VI) acid (1 mol dm^{-3})
Potassium iodide solution (0.1 mol dm^{-3})

Sodium thiosulfate solution (0.1 mol dm^{-3})
Hydrogen peroxide solution (0.1 mol dm^{-3})
Starch solution (1%)
Distilled water
Eye protection

Safety 1 mol dm^{-3} sulfuric(VI) acid is an irritant.

Method

1. Using a measuring cylinder, prepare a mixture of sulfuric(VI) acid and potassium iodide in the conical flask according to the volumes in the table:

Mixture	Volume/cm^3				
	H$_2$SO$_4$	KI	Na$_2$S$_2$O$_3$	H$_2$O$_2$	water
1	10	10	1.0	10	10
2	10	10	1.0	20	0
3	10	20	1.0	10	0

2. Add 1 cm^3 of sodium thiosulfate from a burette followed by 10 cm^3 of distilled water and 5 drops of starch solution.

3. Add 10 cm^3 of hydrogen peroxide, start the stop-watch, swirl the flask and place it on the white tile.

4. Measure the time for the blue starch–iodine complex to appear.

5. Repeat the procedure using different mixtures as outlined in the table.

6. Calculate the initial rate of reaction as 1/time.

7. Deduce the order of reaction with respect to hydrogen peroxide and iodide ions.

Results

Mol/dm^3 in mixture		Time/s	1/time
KI	H$_2$O$_2$		
0.025	0.025	55	0.02
0.025	0.050	25	0.04
0.050	0.025	26	0.04

Notes

1. The equation for the reaction is:

$$H_2O_2 + 2H^+ + 2I^- \rightarrow 2H_2O + I_2$$

2. Doubling the concentration of either hydrogen peroxide or potassium iodide doubled the rate of reaction. Therefore the reaction was first order with respect to these two reagents and second order overall.

3. The rate equation is:

$$\text{Rate} = k[H_2O_2]^1 [I^-]^1$$

4. The mechanism for the reaction is:

slow

(i) $H_2O_2(aq) + I^-(aq) \rightarrow H_2O(l) + IO^-(aq)$

fast

(ii) $H^+(aq) + IO^-(aq) \rightarrow HIO(aq)$

fast

(iii) $HIO(aq) + H^+(aq) + I^-(aq) \rightarrow H_2O(l) + I_2(aq)$

(i) is the rate-determining step because it is the slowest of the three.

5. To convert volume concentrations of H_2O_2 to molarity: e.g. 10 vol H_2O_2. This means that $1\,dm^3$ H_2O_2 will produce $10\,dm^3$ of oxygen when fully decomposed. From equation:

$2H_2O_2 \rightarrow 2H_2O + O_2$

$10\,dm^3 = 10 \div 24 = 0.42$ moles (1 mole of any gas occupies $24\,dm^3$ at room temperature and pressure). Therefore $1\,dm^3$ of 10 vol H_2O_2 contains 0.84 moles. To produce a $0.1\,mol\,dm^{-3}$ solution, dilute $12\,cm^3$ of 10 vol H_2O_2 to $100\,cm^3$ with distilled water.

13.14 To show that amylase will break down starch

I_2/KI solution (dissolve 20 g of
  potassium iodide and 12.7 g of
  iodine in $200\,cm^3$ of distilled water
  and dilute to $1\,dm^3$)
One large potato
Starch solution (1%)
Domestic food blender (must be
  subject to regular portable-
  appliance test)
Net curtain material
Scrubbing brush
Centrifuge (optional)
Distilled water
Test-tubes
Measuring cylinder ($10\,cm^3$)
Access to a refrigerator
Beaker ($500\,cm^3$)
Kettle
Thermometer
Glass rod
Dimple tile

Safety If a centrifuge is used to separate the supernatant from the sediment in the potato extract, make sure the centrifuge conforms to modern safety standards, e.g. the power goes off when the lid is lifted. Do not open the lid of the centrifuge until it has stopped spinning.

Method

1. Clean one large potato under a cold running tap using a scrubbing brush to remove all particles of soil.

2. Put the clean potato in the blender, add $50\,cm^3$ of water and completely liquidise.

3. Filter the mixture through a piece of net curtain material and discard the pulp.

4. Store the liquid in a refrigerator overnight to allow any fine particles to settle out or use a centrifuge.

5. Decant the supernatant which contains the enzyme, amylase.

6. Using a measuring cylinder transfer $1\,cm^3$ of starch solution and $5\,cm^3$ of potato extract to a test-tube.

7. Place the test-tube containing the mixture in a beaker of water at $40\,°C$ together with a test-tube containing $6\,cm^3$ of potato extract and another containing $6\,cm^3$ of starch solution for comparison.

8. Sample the mixture every 5 minutes for 25 minutes by transferring a drop to a dimple tile well with the glass rod, and test it for the presence of starch by adding one drop of I_2/KI solution.

Sample results

Sampling time/min	Starch test		
	Starch	Potato extract	Mixture
5	+	−	+
10	+	−	+
15	+	−	+
20	+	−	−
25	+	−	−

Notes

1. Starch is a polysaccharide made up of α-glucose molecules strung together. During digestion, amylase in saliva breaks down the starch into glucose which is easily absorbed by the gut.

2. I_2/KI solution, in the presence of starch, produces a starch-iodine complex which is blue/black in colour.

3. Two potatoes the size of tennis balls will provide approximately $100\,cm^3$ of extract.

4. Amylase can be catabolic or anabolic depending on the enzyme:substrate ratio in the mixture. On a few occasions, this experiment has shown that starch was digested after 15 minutes but then had begun to build up again by the next sampling, so these results can be expected:

Sampling time/min	Starch test		
	Starch	Potato extract	Mixture
5	+	−	+
10	+	−	+
15	+	−	−
20	+	−	+
25	+	−	+

13.15 Order of reaction with respect to oxygen in the 'Bluebottle Experiment'

0.1% methylene blue solution in ethanol ($50\,cm^3$)
Conical flask ($250\,cm^3$)
Sodium hydroxide pellets
Glucose
Spatula

Distilled water
Measuring cylinder ($250\,cm^3$)
Top-pan balance
Stop-watch
Eye protection

Safety Sodium hydroxide pellets are corrosive. Ethanol is highly flammable.

Method

1. Prepare the 'Bluebottle' by dissolving 3 g of sodium hydroxide pellets in $150\,cm^3$ of distilled water in the conical flask. Add 5 g of glucose and swirl until dissolved. Then add $2.5\,cm^3$ of methylene blue solution, close the flask with a bung and shake to mix. The mixture turns colourless but the blue colour re-appears after about a minute.

2. Measure the time t for all the blue colour to re-appear for different number of shakes of the 'Bluebottle'.

3. Plot graphs of rate on the y-axis against number of shakes N, $\log_{10}$ of number of shakes and the reciprocal of the number of shakes.

Sample results

N	$\log_{10}N$	$1/N$	t/s	Rate($1/t \times 10^{-3}$)
1	0	1.00	29	345
5	0.7	0.20	92	109
10	1.0	0.10	145	69
20	1.3	0.05	170	59
50	1.7	0.02	187	53

Notes

1. In alkaline conditions, glucose reduces the methylene blue to a colourless form. Shaking the mixture allows oxygen from the air to dissolve in the mixture and this oxidises the methylene blue back to its blue form.

2. The number of shakes is proportional to the concentration of oxygen which dissolves in the mixture from the air.

3. Only the plot of rate(in terms of 1/time) against the reciprocal of the number of shakes was linear, so the reaction was second order with respect to the dissolved oxygen concentration.

14 REVERSIBLE REACTIONS AND CHEMICAL EQUILIBRIUM

If two reactants A and B react together to form products C and D, then it is possible for C and D to react together to form A and B. So a reversible reaction is a reaction that may proceed in either direction depending on the applied conditions. When the rates of the two opposing processes are equal, the system is in equilibrium. In an equilibrium system the products of the forward reaction are being formed at the same rate as they are being decomposed so the equilibrium is dynamic. Both forward and reverse reactions take place simultaneously and continuously. Reversible reactions are shown by a double half arrow between reactants and products in the equation:

$$A + B \rightleftharpoons C + D$$

The Equilibrium law states that the concentration in mol dm^{-3} of the products raised to the power of their stoichiometric coefficients divided by the concentration in mol dm^{-3} of the reactants raised to their stoichiometric coefficients is a constant for a given equilibrium system. This constant is called the equilibrium constant. So, for the reaction:

$$aA + bB \rightleftharpoons cC + dD$$

$$K_c = \frac{[C]^c[D]^d}{[A]^a[B]^b}$$

For gaseous equilibria, the equilibrium constant can be expressed in terms of partial pressures of the gases in the equilibrium mixture:

$$K_p = \frac{(p_C)^c(p_D)^d}{(p_A)^a(p_B)^b}$$

The partial pressure of a gas in a gaseous mixture is the pressure which that gas would have if it, alone, occupied the same volume of space. The total pressure of a mixture of gases in equilibrium is the sum of the partial pressures of the components. The mole fraction of each gas in the equilibrium mixture = partial pressure ÷ total pressure, so concentrations can be converted to partial pressures by:

Partial pressure = mole fraction × total pressure

For ideal gases, K_c and K_p conversions can be done by applying the following relationship:

$$K_p = K_c(RT)^{\Delta n}$$

where Δn is the number of moles of products – number of moles of reactants in the balanced equation, R = gas constant and T = absolute temperature.

Changes in the concentration of particles in the reactant/product mixture, temperature and, for gaseous mixtures, pressure, will change the position of the equilibrium according to Le Chatelier's principle: If a constraint is applied to a system in equilibrium, then the equilibrium position will move so as to annul the constraint. In other words, the forward reaction will be favoured by increasing the concentration of reactants or decreasing the concentration of products, by raising the temperature of an endothermic reaction and lowering the temperature of an exothermic reaction, and vice versa. In gaseous reactions in which the forward reaction produces a decrease in the number of particles, increasing the pressure will favour the forward reaction, and vice versa. However, only temperature changes affect the value of the equilibrium constant because the activation energies of the forward and reverse reactions are different.

Catalysts affect both opposing processes to the same extent and therefore do not affect the position of the equilibrium, nor the value of the equilibrium constant. However, equilibrium is established quicker by the use of catalysts, hence their importance in industry where production rates need to be economic.

14.1 Effect of heat on hydrated copper(II) sulfate(VI) and subsequent addition of water to the anhydrous product

Test-tubes
Retort stand and clamp
Bunsen burner
Teat pipette(dropper)
Distilled water

Spatula
Copper(II) sulfate(VI)-5-water
  ($CuSO_4.5H_2O$)
Eye protection

Safety Copper(II) sulfate(VI) is harmful.

Method

1. Hold the test-tube in the clamp and stand and add one rounded spatula measure of copper(II) sulfate(VI) crystals.

2. Heat gently at first and then more strongly using the Bunsen burner and observe the colour change in the copper(II) sulfate(VI).

3. Stop heating and allow the test-tube to cool to room temperature.

4. Put a thermometer in the test-tube ensuring good contact with the solid and add distilled water, dropwise, using the pipette. Observe any colour and temperature changes that occur.

Sample results

Effect of heating the hydrated copper(II) sulfate(VI) crystals: colour changed from blue to white. Condensation occurred at the top of the test-tube. Effect of adding cold distilled water to the previously heated copper(II) sulfate(VI) crystals: colour changed from white to blue and there was a considerable rise in temperature.

Notes

1. Heat needs to be applied in order to remove the water of crystallisation from the hydrated copper(II) sulfate(VI):

$$CuSO_4.5H_2O \xrightarrow{\text{Heat}} CuSO_4 + 5H_2O$$

This process is endothermic.

2. Adding water to the anhydrous copper(II) sulfate(VI) reverses the process which is accompanied by a rise in temperature (exothermic) and a restoration of the blue colour.

$$CuSO_4 + 5H_2O \rightarrow CuSO_4.5H_2O$$

3. Copper(II) sulfate(VI) crystals are blue in colour because the copper(II) ion forms four dative covalent bonds with each of four water molecules to produce the $[Cu(H_2O)_4]^{2+}$ complex ion.

14.2 Effect of heat on hydrated cobalt(II) chloride and subsequent addition of water to the anhydrous product

Apparatus/reagents as for 14.1. but substituting hydrated cobalt(II) chloride for the hydrated copper(II) sulfate(VI).
Eye protection

Safety Cobalt(II) chloride is a category 2 carcinogen by inhalation and therefore toxic. Avoid skin contact as it may cause sensitisation. Teacher demonstration only.

Sample results

Effect of heating hydrated cobalt(II) chloride: The dark red crystals changed colour to dark blue and condensation occurred at the top of the test-tube. Effect of adding distilled water to the previously heated hydrated cobalt(II) chloride: The dark blue solid changed back to dark red and this was accompanied by a rise in temperature.

Notes

1. In hydrated cobalt(II) chloride, the cobalt forms six dative covalent bonds with each of six molecules of water to produce $[Co(H_2O)_6]^{2+}$ complex ion which is responsible for the dark red colour. Heat dehydrates the compound and cobalt then complexes with four chloride ions to form the $CoCl_4{}^{2-}$ ion which is blue.

2. Adding water to the previously heated cobalt(II) chloride reverses the process.

14.3 Effect of adding propanone to aqueous cobalt(II) chloride solution followed by the addition of water

Test-tubes

Bungs

Distilled water

Propanone

Hydrated cobalt(II) chloride

Spatula

Measuring cylinder ($10\,cm^3$)

Eye protection

Safety **Propanone is highly flammable. Cobalt(II) chloride is a category 2 carcinogen by inhalation and therefore toxic. Avoid skin contact as it may cause sensitisation. Teacher demonstration only.**

Method

1. Transfer 0.5 g (1 level spoon spatula measure) of cobalt(II) chloride crystals to a test-tube and add $1\,cm^3$ of distilled water. Close the tube with a bung and shake to dissolve.

2. Remove the bung and, using a measuring cylinder, add $7\,cm^3$ of propanone, replace the bung and shake. Observe the effect.

3. Remove the bung again and add $5\,cm^3$ of distilled water, replace the bung and shake. Observe the effect.

Sample results

Effect of adding propanone: Solution turned from red to blue.

Effect of adding water to the cobalt(II) chloride/propanone mixture: Solution turned from blue back to red.

Notes

1. The reaction is a reversible de-hydration/re-hydration of the cobalt chloride. See 14.2 Note 1.

2. The propanone is the dehydrating agent.

14.4 Effect of adding sodium hydroxide followed by hydrochloric acid to iron(III) thiocyanate solution

Iron(III) chloride solution
  (0.05 mol dm^{-3})
Potassium thiocyanate solution
  (0.05 mol dm^{-3})
Distilled water
Measuring cylinders (10 cm^3 and
  25 cm^3)

Hydrochloric acid (0.5 mol dm^{-3})
Sodium hydroxide solution
  (0.5 mol dm^{-3})
Boiling tubes with bungs
Eye protection

Safety 0.5 mol dm^{-3} sodium hydroxide solution is corrosive.

Method

1. Using a measuring cylinder, transfer 1 cm^3 of potassium thiocyanate solution and 1 cm^3 of iron(III) chloride solution to a boiling tube. An intense blood-red coloured solution is formed.

2. Add 20 cm^3 of sodium hydroxide solution, close the tube with a bung and invert to mix. Observe the colour change.

3. Remove the bung and add 20 cm^3 of hydrochloric acid. Replace the bung and invert to mix. Observe the colour change again.

Sample results

The blood-red colour disappears on adding sodium hydroxide and is restored by adding hydrochloric acid.

Notes

1. When iron(III) chloride and potassium thiocyanate solutions are mixed, the blood-red colour is due to the formation of an iron(III)-thiocyanate complex according the following equation:

$$FeCl_3 + KCNS \rightarrow Fe(CNS)Cl_2 + KCl$$

2. The iron(III) thiocyanate complex decomposes in alkaline conditions and reforms in acidic conditions:

$$[FeCNS]^{2+} \rightleftharpoons Fe^{3+} + CNS^-$$

14.5 Reversible reduction and re-oxidation of iron(III)

Iron(III) chloride solution (0.1 mol dm^{-3})
Hydrogen peroxide (2.5 vol)
Sodium hydroxide solution (0.5 mol dm^{-3})
Sodium sulfate(IV)

Spatula
Hydrochloric acid (0.5 mol dm^{-3})
Boiling tubes with bungs
Bunsen burner
Measuring cylinder (10 cm^3)
Eye protection

Safety 0.5 mol dm^{-3} sodium hydroxide solution is corrosive. Sodium sulfate(IV) is harmful and, when in contact with acid, produces sulfur dioxide gas which is toxic. The experiment should be carried out in a well ventilated area because sulfur dioxide is produced when the mixture is warmed. Eye protection must be worn.

Method

1. Using a measuring cylinder, transfer 1 cm^3 of iron(III) chloride solution to a boiling tube and confirm that the iron is in the 3+ state by adding sodium hydroxide to produce a brown precipitate of iron(III) hydroxide.

2. Transfer another 1 cm^3 of iron(III) chloride to another boiling tube, add one spatula measure (approximately 0.5 g) of sodium sulfate(IV) and warm it gently over a Bunsen flame. The orange colour should disappear and the solution should appear colourless.

3. Add 35 cm^3 of sodium hydroxide solution, close the tube with a bung and invert to mix. Observe the colour of the precipitate.

4. Add 2 cm^3 of hydrogen peroxide and note the colour change.

Sample results

Effect of sodium hydroxide following treatment of the solution with acid and sodium sulfate(IV): Blue-green gelatinous precipitate formed.

Effect of adding hydrogen peroxide to the mixture: Blue-green precipitate changed colour to orange-brown.

Notes

1. The sulfur dioxide reduces the iron(III) to iron(II) which forms a blue-green gelatinous precipitate of iron(II) hydroxide with sodium hydroxide.

2. Hydrogen peroxide oxidises the iron(II) hydroxide to iron(III) hydroxide and the colour changes from blue-green to orange-brown.

14.6 Effect of adding sodium hydroxide to bromine water and cyclohexane followed by addition of hydrochloric acid

Measuring cylinder
Bromine water (0.5 mol dm^{-3})
Test-tube with cork
Sodium hydroxide solution
　　(0.5 mol dm^{-3})

Hydrochloric acid (0.5 mol dm^{-3})
Cyclohexane
Eye protection

Safety 0.5 mol dm^{-3} sodium hydroxide solution is corrosive. Bromine water is toxic and corrosive (at this concentration) and should be used in a fume cupboard. Avoid skin contact. Treat spillage with sodium thiosulfate solution. Cyclohexane is highly flammable and harmful.

Method

1. Using a measuring cylinder transfer 1cm^3 of bromine water and 1 cm^3 of cyclohexane to a test-tube, close the tube with a cork, shake the tube vigorously and set aside for the layers to separate. Note the colour of the organic layer.

2. Remove the cork and add 5 cm^3 of sodium hydroxide solution, replace the cork, shake the tube vigorously again and set aside for the layers to separate. Note the change in appearance of the organic layer.

3. Remove the cork and add 5 cm^3 of hydrochloric acid, replace the cork, shake the tube vigorously and set aside for the layers to separate. Again note the appearance of the organic layer.

Sample results

Effect of adding cyclohexane to bromine water: Bromine transferred to the organic layer which appeared orange in colour.

Effect of adding sodium hydroxide: Organic layer was decolorised.

Effect of adding hydrochloric acid: Orange colour restored in the organic layer.

Notes

1. Sodium hydroxide converts bromine to bromate(V) which is colourless and soluble in the aqueous layer.

2. Hydrochloric acid reverses the process and the bromine is soluble in the organic layer:

$$3Br_2 + 3H_2O \rightleftharpoons 5HBr + HBrO_3$$

3. Do not use a rubber bung with the cyclohexane because the cyclohexane may react with the rubber.

14.7 Factors affecting the acidified cobalt(II) chloride equilibrium

Cobalt(II) chloride solution
(10% $CoCl_2.6H_2O$ in 50% HCl)
Four boiling tubes
Measuring cylinder (100 cm^3)
Three beakers (250 cm^3)
Two teat pipettes (droppers)

Concentrated hydrochloric acid
Crushed ice
Bunsen burner
Tripod and gauze
Eye protection

Safety Concentrated hydrochloric acid is corrosive. Cobalt(II) chloride is a category 2 carcinogen by inhalation and therefore toxic. Avoid skin contact as it may cause sensitisation. Responsible pupils could handle the solution.

Method

1. Using a measuring cylinder transfer 20 cm^3 of the cobalt(II) chloride solution to each of four boiling tubes.

2. The following equilibrium is set up:

$$[Co(H_2O)_6]^{2+} + 4Cl^- \rightleftharpoons [CoCl_4]^{2-} + 6H_2O$$

endothermic   exothermic

Show the effect of changing the concentration of reactants by:

(i) Adding concentrated hydrochloric acid to one tube

(ii) Adding water to another tube

Show the effect of changing temperature by:

(i) Placing one tube in boiling water

(ii) Placing another tube in crushed ice

Sample results

Test	Observation
Adding water	solution turned pink
Adding conc. HCl	solution turned blue
In boiling water	solution turned blue
In crushed ice	solution turned pink

Note

The changes in the equilibrium position are in accordance with Le Chatelier's principle: If a constraint is applied to a system in equilibrium, the equilibrium position will move to annul the constraint.

14.8 Determination of the equilibrium constant for the formation of an ester

Two conical flasks (250 cm^3)
    with bungs
Concentrated ethanoic acid
Ethanol
Concentrated sulfuric(VI) acid
Three teat pipettes (droppers)
Beaker (100 cm^3)
Sodium hydroxide solution
    (1 mol dm^{-3})

Phenolphthalein
Burette (50 cm^3)
Retort stand and clamp
Marker pen
Top-pan balance
Eye protection

Safety 1 mol dm^{-3} sodium hydroxide solution is corrosive. Concentrated ethanoic acid and concentrated sulfuric(VI) acid are both corrosive. Phenolphthalein is a purgative and is dissolved in a highly flammable solvent. Ethanol is highly flammable.

Method

1. Place a conical flask on the pan of the balance and, using a dropper, add exactly 6.0 g of concentrated ethanoic acid and 6.2 g of ethanol. These quantities are equivalent to 0.1 mole.

2. Add one drop of concentrated sulfuric(VI) acid, close the flask with a bung and swirl the flask to mix the contents.

3. Set up a blank by adding about $20\,cm^3$ of distilled water to another conical flask followed by one drop of concentrated sulphuric acid using the same dropper as before. Close the flask with a bung and swirl to mix. Identify the flasks using the marker pen.

4. Set the flasks aside for one week at room temperature to equilibrate.

5. After one week, titrate the mixtures against standard sodium hydroxide solution ($1\,mol\,dm^{-3}$) using phenolphthalein indicator and record the volume of sodium hydroxide solution needed to neutralise the acidity in the mixtures.

6. The difference between the two titres gives the volume of ethanoic acid in the equilibrium mixture.

Sample results

Blank titre = $1.2\,cm^3$

Equilibrium mixture titre = $34.2\,cm^3$

Calculations

Volume of alkali needed to neutralise the ethanoic acid in the equilibrium mixture = $34.2 - 1.2 = 33.0\,cm^3$

Converting to moles: $33.0 \div 1000 \times 1 = 0.033\,moles$

From the equation:

$$CH_3COOH + NaOH \rightarrow CH_3COONa + H_2O$$

Moles of ethanoic acid present in the equilibrium mixture = $0.033\,moles$

From the equation:

$$CH_3COOH + C_2H_5OH \rightleftharpoons CH_3COOC_2H_5 + H_2O$$

Mole composition of the equilibrium mixture:

$CH_3COOH = 0.033$

$C_2H_5OH = 0.033$

$CH_3COOC_2H_5 = 0.067$ (Note: $0.1 - 0.033$)

$H_2O = 0.067$

Equilibrium constant $K_c = (0.067 \div V \times 0.067 \div V)/(0.033 \div V \times 0.033 \div V)$

$= 4.12$. (Note: All volume V terms cancel)

Note

The experiment could be adapted to investigate the time required to reach equilibrium by setting up seven identical mixtures plus a blank and titrating one mixture each day. Then show the rate of decrease in the ethanoic concentration by plotting a line graph of ethanoic acid concentration against time.

14.9 Determination of the dissociation constant for bromophenol blue indicator (a weak acid)

Bromophenol blue indicator solution:
    Add 1 g of the solid to 15 cm^3 of
    0.1 mol dm^{-3} NaOH and dilute the
    solution to 1 dm^3 with distilled
    water
Sodium hydroxide solution
    (4 mol dm^{-3})
Concentrated hydrochloric acid
Measuring cylinder (10 cm^3)

18 test-tubes
Double test-tube rack
Methanoic acid solution
    (0.02 mol dm^{-3})
Sodium methanoate solution
    (0.02 mol dm^{-3})
Distilled water
Four teat pipettes
Eye protection

Safety Concentrated hydrochloric acid and 4 mol dm^{-3} sodium hydroxide solution are both corrosive. 0.1 mol dm^{-3} sodium hydroxide is irritant.

Method

1. Add one drop of concentrated hydrochloric acid to 5 cm^3 of bromophenol blue indicator solution. Label this solution 1.

2. Add one drop of 4 mol dm^{-3} sodium hydroxide solution to 5 cm^3 of bromophenol blue indicator solution. Label this solution 2.

3. Arrange 18 test-tubes in nine pairs, one behind the other, in a double test-tube rack.

4. Using a measuring cylinder, put 10 cm^3 of distilled water into each test tube and add drops of solutions 1 and 2 as follows:

Tube:	1	2	3	4	5	6	7	8	9
Drops of soln 1:	1	2	3	4	5	6	7	8	9

Tube:	10	11	12	13	14	15	16	17	18
Drops of soln 2:	9	8	7	6	5	4	3	2	1

When looking through a pair of tubes, the colour seen will be due to the colour of the solutions in both tubes. Mole concentrations are proportional to the number of drops added.

5. Mix 5 cm^3 of methanoic acid with 5 cm^3 of sodium methanoate solution. Add 10 drops of bromophenol blue indicator solution and compare the colour with the colour of a pair of tubes which most nearly matches it.

6. Given that the dissociation constant for methanoic acid is 0.0002, calculate the pH from:

$$pH = -\log_{10}K_a - \log_{10}\frac{[\text{HCOOH}]}{[\text{HCOO}^-]}$$

7. Calculate K_a for bromophenol blue.

Sample results

The colour of the methanoic acid–sodium methanoate mixture resembled the colour of tubes 3 and 12.

Calculations

pH of the methanoic acid/sodium methanoate mixture
$= -\log_{10}0.0002 - \log_{10}1$ (because mixture was made up of equal conc. of acid and salt) $= 3.7$

The ratio between particles of undissociated indicator and fully dissociated indicator particles at pH 3.7 $= 3 : 7$ (tubes 3 and 12).

Rearranging the equation:

$pK_a =$

pH $- \log_{10}$ [undissociated indicator] $\div$ [fully dissociated indicator]
$= 3.7 - \log_{10}(3 \div 7)$

$= 3.7 - (-0.37)$

$= 4.07$

$K_a = 1.18 \times 10^{-4}$

Notes

1. pH indicators are weak acids whose conjugate base has a different colour from that of the acid.

2. Indicators change colour when the pH of the solution equals the pK_a value for the indicator.

3. When the pH of the solution is less than the pK_a value then the indicator is undissociated. When the pH is greater than the pK_a value then the indicator fully dissociates. Solution 1 contains undissociated indicator and solution 2 contains fully dissociated indicator.

4. When the concentrations of undissociated indicator and fully dissociated indicator are equal the colour is exactly at the colour change point.

5. It is important to know the dissociation constant of indicators so that the most suitable can be chosen for a particular titration, because the equivalence point of different titration mixtures occurs at different values of pH.

14.10 Determination of the solubility product for silver iodate(V)

Ten conical flasks with bungs ($100\,cm^3$)

Silver nitrate(V) solution ($0.005\,mol\,dm^{-3}$)

Potassium iodate(V) solution ($0.005\,mol\,dm^{-3}$)

Measuring cylinder ($100\,cm^3$)

Starch solution (1%)

Sodium thiosulfate solution ($0.025\,mol\,dm^{-3}$)

Potassium iodide solution ($0.004\,mol\,dm^{-3}$)

Sulfuric(VI) acid ($1\,mol\,dm^{-3}$)

Potassium iodide

Spatula

Burette ($50\,cm^3$)

Eye protection

Safety $1\,mol\,dm^{-3}$ sulfuric(VI) acid is irritant.

Method

1. Using a measuring cylinder, make up the following mixtures in conical flasks:

Mixture	Silver nitrate(V)/ cm^3	Potassium iodate(V)/ cm^3
A	60	40
B	55	45
C	50	50
D	45	55
E	40	60

2. Close the flasks with bungs, shake the mixtures and leave them to stand overnight at room temperature to equilibrate.

3. Filter the mixtures using dry filter paper, funnels and flasks.

4. Using a measuring cylinder, transfer 75 cm^3 of filtrate to another conical flask. Add 1 cm^3 of starch solution followed by 20 cm^3 of sulfuric(VI) acid and titrate against 0.004 mol dm^{-3} potassium iodide. The end point is reached when the titration mixture changes to its first blue-green colour.

5. Using $Ag^+:I^-::1:1$, calculate the concentration of silver ions in the mixture.

6. To the same titration mixture, add 1 g of solid potassium iodide followed by 20 cm^3 of sulfuric(VI) acid. Swirl the flask and titrate the liberated iodine using 0.025 mol dm^{-3} sodium thiosulfate. The end point is reached when the blue colour is just discharged.

7. Using $IO_3^-:S_2O_3^{2-}::1:6$, calculate the concentration of iodate(V) ions in the mixture.

8. Calculate the solubility product for silver iodate(V) in each mixture which should be constant at 2×10^{-8} mol^2 dm^{-6}

Sample results

Mixture A required 2.64 cm^3 of 0.004 mol dm^{-3} KI and 2.54 cm^3 of 0.025 mol dm^{-3} Na$_2$S$_2$O$_3$.

Concentration of Ag^+ ions $= \dfrac{2.64}{1000} \times 0.004 \times \dfrac{1000}{75}$

$$= 1.41 \times 10^{-4} \text{ mol dm}^{-3}$$

Concentration of IO_3^- ions $= \dfrac{2.54}{1000} \times 0.025 \times \dfrac{1000}{75}$

$$= 1.41 \times 10^{-4} \text{ mol dm}^{-3}$$

$K_{sp} = [1.41 \times 10^{-4} \text{ mol dm}^{-3}][\, 1.41 \times 10^{-4} \text{ mol dm}^{-3}]$

$$= 1.99 \times 10^{-8} \text{ mol}^2 \text{ dm}^{-6}$$

Notes

1. Equations for the reactions involved in the titrations are:

   Titration 1: $Ag^+(aq) + I^-(aq) \rightarrow AgI(s)$

   When all of the silver is precipitated, the $I^-(aq)$ begins to react with the iodate(V) ions to liberate iodine which forms a complex with starch to produce a dark blue colour. Silver iodide is pale yellow so the mixture takes on a green-blue colour at the end point of the titration.

   Titration 2: Iodate(V) ions oxidise iodide in the added solid potassium iodide:

   $$IO_3^-(aq) + I^-(aq) + 6H^+(aq) \rightarrow 3I_2(aq) + 3H_2O(l)$$

   The liberated iodine reacts with the starch to form the dark blue coloured complex. The $S_2O_3^{2-}(aq)$ ions reduce the iodine back to $I^-(aq)$ and the starch-iodine complex is destroyed. This is the end point of the second titration.

   $$I_2(aq) + 2S_2O_3^{2-}(aq) \rightarrow 2I^-(aq) + S_4O_6^{2-}(aq)$$

15 ORGANIC CHEMISTRY

Organic chemistry is the chemistry of compounds containing carbon. It is called organic chemistry because many of the first known compounds containing carbon were obtained from living things. Of the five million or so compounds known to chemists, 80% contain carbon. The relative abundance of carbon on Earth is only 0.01%. This huge discrepancy indicates that carbon has some rather unusual bonding characteristics, e.g. it can participate in bonding with other carbon atoms (catenation) to form long chains, branched chains and ring structures. The bonding can be single or multiple.

Organic molecules formed from a series of many repeating simple molecular units are called polymers. Polythene, polyvinyl chloride, and polystyrene are common examples, to name but a few.

Crude oil, which is the fossilised remains of unicellular marine life, is a mixture of many different organic compounds which after separation produces fuel, lubricants, detergents and polymers.

15.1 To show that material from living things contains carbon

Test-tube fitted with a bung and a
    single bend delivery tube
Copper(II) oxide
Spatula
Limewater
Clamp and stand
Bunsen burner
Jam-jar lid (or watch glass)

Lard
Butter
Starch
Margarine
Anhydrous cobalt(II) chloride paper
Eye protection
Forceps

Safety Copper(II) oxide is harmful. **Remove the test-tube of limewater from the delivery tube before removing the Bunsen burner in order to avoid suck-back as the hot test-tube cools. Handle the cobalt(II) chloride paper with forceps because cobalt(II) chloride is toxic.**

Method

1. Take a rounded spatula measure of the substance and mix it with an equal quantity of copper(II) oxide.

2. Put the mixture in the bottom of the test-tube, fit the bung and delivery tube and support the top of the test-tube in the clamp and stand.

3. Quarter fill another test-tube with limewater and hold it so that the end of delivery tube is submerged in the limewater.

4. Heat the mixture of copper(II) oxide and substance under test and observe the change in the appearance of the limewater as the mixture is heated.

5. Test the liquid which condenses at the top of the tube containing the heated mixture with anhydrous cobalt(II) chloride paper.

6. Examine the heated mixture for traces of copper.

Sample results

With each substance, the limewater turned milky and the condensed liquid turned anhydrous cobalt(II) chloride paper from blue to pink. After heating, the mixtures contained brown specks of copper.

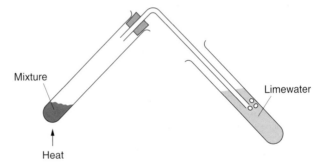

Mixture

Limewater

Heat

Figure 15.1 Testing for carbon dioxide.

Notes

1. The limewater turned milky because carbon dioxide was produced.

$$Ca(OH)_2(aq) + CO_2(g) \rightarrow CaCO_3(s) + H_2O(l)$$

2. The condensed liquid was water.

3. The equation for the reaction of the substances with copper(II) oxide:

Carbon and hydrogen + CuO CO_2 + H_2O + Cu
in the mixture

228

15.2 Fractional distillation of crude oil

Thermometer (0–360 °C)

Boiling tube with a side arm connected to a single-bend delivery tube

Bung with hole to take the thermometer and which fits the boiling tube

Mineral wool

Crude oil, see Note 3.

Four test-tubes

Jam-jar lid

Damp cloth

Retort stand and clamp

Bunsen burner

Wooden splint

Eye protection

Safety screen

Access to fume cupboard

Safety The demonstration should be carried out behind a safety screen. Heating may be done using a Bunsen burner because the amount of highly flammable material is small. However, have a damp cloth ready to extinguish any fires. The fractions should be burnt in a fume cupboard.

Method

1. Set up the apparatus as shown in Figure 15.2.

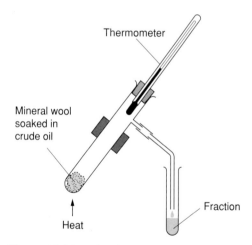

Figure 15.2 Fractional distillation of crude oil.

2. Heat the mineral wool soaked in crude oil and collect fractions with the following boiling points: 0–70, 71–120, 121–170 and 171–220 °C.

3. Note the colour of each fraction.

4. In the fume cupboard, pour each fraction in turn into the jam-jar lid and ignite it with a burning splint.

5. Note the flame colour and how much smoke is produced.

Sample results

Fraction	b.p./°C	Colour	How the fraction burned	
			Flame colour	How much smoke
Petrol	0–70	Colourless	Pale yellow	Very little
Paraffin	71–120	Pale yellow	Yellow	More smoke
Diesel	121–170	Yellow	Brighter yellow	More smoke still
Lubri-cating oil	171–220	Darker yellow	Orange	Sooty

Notes

1. The results show that crude oil is a mixture of substances which can be separated according to their boiling points.

2. The sootiness and colour of the flame when the fraction burned is an indicator of the number of carbon atoms in the molecules. The higher the boiling point, the greater the number of carbon atoms.

3. Crude oil is made up by mixing: Liquid paraffin (medicinal), 55 cm^3; paraffin oil (kerosene), 20 cm^3; white spirit, 11 cm^3; petroleum ether (b.p. 100–120 °C), 4 cm^3; petroleum ether (b.p. 60–80 °C), 6 cm^3; petroleum ether (b.p. 80–100 °C), 4 cm^3. Add one rounded spatula measure of powdered carbon to make the mixture look realistic.

15.3 Destructive distillation of coal

See Figure 15.3 for apparatus/reagents, plus forceps, litmus paper.

Safety The demonstration should be carried out behind a safety screen and in a fume cupboard and eye protection must be worn. The gas from the chimney contains toxic and corrosive products which may cause asthma attacks in susceptible people. Handle the boiling tube containing the condensed phenols carefully because they are harmful to the skin.

Method

1. Assemble the apparatus as shown, heat the powdered coal strongly with a roaring Bunsen burner and ignite the gas escaping from the 'chimney'.

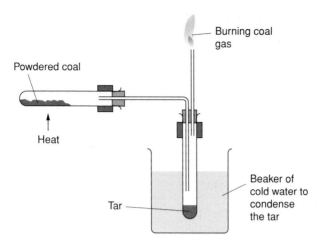

Figure 15.3 Destructive distillation of coal.

2. When the production of gas ceases, stop heating and allow the apparatus to cool.

3. Empty the residue onto a tripod and gauze and compare its appearance with the appearance of the original coal.

4. Heat the residue and also the original coal from a roaring inverted overhead Bunsen burner and compare the combustion of the two materials.

Sample results

The gas escaping from the 'chimney' burned with a yellow smoky flame. The residue was grey, dull and porous whereas the original coal was solid and black with a shiny appearance. The residue just glowed when heated whereas the original coal burned with a yellow sooty flame.

Notes

1. The gas produced was 'coal gas' (carbon monoxide) which was used as a domestic fuel before the discovery of 'North Sea gas' (methane).

2. The residue was coke, a smokeless fuel.

3. The brown liquid which condensed in the boiling tube immersed in water was 'Coal Tar', a mixture of phenolic substances used for making soap.

4. Bituminous coal gives better results than anthracite. However the experiment could be extended to compare these two fuels.

5. Ammonia is a by-product from the distillation of coal. Before burning the coal gas at the chimney, hold a piece of damp red litmus paper with forceps over the chimney. The litmus paper turns blue.

15.4 Products of combustion

For apparatus/reagents, see Figure 15.4.

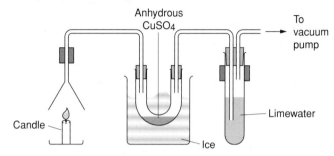

Figure 15.4 Products of combustion.

Safety Anhydrous copper(II) sulfate(VI) is harmful and a solution of the hydrated salt is irritant. Eye protection should be worn.

Method

1. Assemble the apparatus as shown in Figure 15.4.

2. Light the candle and turn on the water tap to provide the vacuum.

3. Observe the changes in the appearance of the anhydrous copper(II) sulfate(VI) and the limewater.

Sample results

The limewater turned milky and the anhydrous copper(II) sulfate(VI) changed colour from white to blue.

Notes

1. The limewater detected carbon dioxide and the anhydrous copper(II) sulfate(VI) detected water.

2. The results show that the burning candle produced carbon dioxide and water:

Hydrocarbon $+ O_2 \rightarrow CO_2 + H_2O$

3. If the gap between the candle flame and the funnel is too small, there will be insufficient air for the candle to burn.

15.5 Tests for unsaturation in organic compounds

Potassium manganate(VII) solution
    ($0.2\,\text{mol dm}^{-3}$)
Bromine water ($0.5\,\text{mol dm}^{-3}$)
Sulfuric(VI) acid ($1\,\text{mol dm}^{-3}$)
Cyclohexane

Cyclohexene
Five test-tubes with corks
Teat pipette (dropper)
Measuring cylinder ($10\,\text{cm}^3$)
Eye protection

Safety $1\,\text{mol dm}^{-3}$ **sulfuric(VI) acid is irritant. Bromine water at this concentration is harmful and irritant. Treat spillage with aqueous sodium thiosulfate solution. The hydrocarbons are highly flammable and irritant. Do not use rubber bungs because of a reaction with the organic compounds.**

Method

1. Using the measuring cylinder, transfer $1\,\text{cm}^3$ of cyclohexane to each of two test-tubes.

2. Mix equal quantities of potassium manganate(VII) solution and sulfuric(VI) acid in a test-tube.

3. Add a few drops of the acidified potassium manganate(VII) solution to one test-tube containing cyclohexane, and a a few drops of bromine water to the other.

4. Close the test-tubes with corks and shake them vigorously.

5. Repeat the procedure with cyclohexene.

Sample results

Test	Observations	
	Cyclohexane	Cyclohexene
Acidified KMnO$_4$	No change	Decolorised
Bromine water	No change	Decolorised

Notes

1. A compound is unsaturated if it contains multiple bonds between carbon atoms. Cyclohexane is saturated because all bonds between carbon atoms are single bonds. A cyclohexene molecule contains one double bond between two adjacent carbon atoms and therefore is unsaturated.

2. Unsaturated compounds undergo addition reactions, for example:

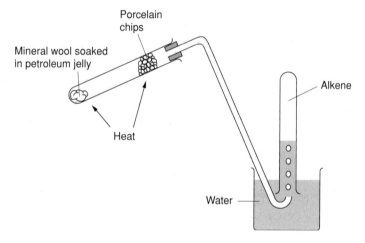

15.6 Cracking an alkane

For apparatus/reagents, see Figure 15.5, and Experiment 15.5.

Figure 15.5 Cracking an alkane.

Safety The demonstration should be carried out behind a safety screen. Bromine water is harmful and irritant. Treat spillage with aqueous sodium thiosulfate solution. It is important to remove the delivery tube from the tub of water before removing the Bunsen burner in order to avoid the danger of suck-back. If a suck-back occurs, the cold water will break the hot boiling tube and the gases inside will catch fire. Keep a damp cloth available as a precaution against this happening.

Method

1. Assemble the apparatus as shown and heat the porcelain chips. Then heat the mineral wool soaked in petroleum jelly. Move the Bunsen

burner backwards and forwards under the mineral wool and the porcelain chips.

2. Discard the first tube of gas collected because this contains mainly air displaced from the inside of the apparatus.

3. Collect three test-tubes of gas.

4. Test the gas inside the test-tubes with a burning splint, bromine water and acidified potassium manganate(VII) as described in 15.5.

5. Carry out these tests on the original petroleum jelly.

Sample results

Test	Gas	Petroleum jelly
Burning splint	Ignited with a clean pale yellow flame	No effect
Bromine water	Decolorised	No effect
Acidified $KMnO_4$	Decolorised	No effect

Notes

1. Soaking the mineral wool in petroleum jelly will be more easily accomplished if the petroleum jelly is melted by warming it in a boiling tube over a Bunsen burner.

2. The petroleum jelly cracked to produce an alkene and an alkane with fewer carbon atoms than the original petroleum jelly, e.g. the cracking of nonane:

$$C_9H_{20} \rightarrow C_7H_{16} + C_2H_4$$

Aluminium oxide in the porcelain acts as a catalyst.

3. The positive test for unsaturation is evidence for the presence of alkenes in the products of the reaction.

4. Ethene can be prepared by applying exactly the same procedure to ethanol in place of the petroleum jelly. The aluminium oxide in the porcelain dehydrates the ethanol:

$$C_2H_5OH \xrightarrow{Al_2O_3} C_2H_4 + H_2O$$

15.7 Polymerisation

Polymerisation is the formation of long chains and networks of repeating units to give molecules of high relative molecular mass.

15.7.1 Production of nylon

Beaker (100 cm³)
A 3% solution of dodecanedioyl
   dichloride in cyclohexane
A solution of hexane–1,6–diamine in
   0.8% sodium hydroxide solution

Forceps
Glass rod
Measuring cylinder (100 cm³)
Eye protection

Safety Dodecanedioyl dichloride is corrosive and the cyclohexane in which it is dissolved is highly flammable. Hexane–1,6–diamine in 0.8% aqueous sodium hydroxide is irritant. Do not touch the nylon with the fingers unless it is well washed. The nylon forms a fine tube which may contain a small amount of the lower layer.

Method

1. Using the measuring cylinder, transfer 10 cm³ of hexane–1,6–diamine solution to the beaker.

2. Add 10 cm³ of dodecanedioyl chloride solution. Do not stir.

3. Using forceps, draw a thread of nylon from the interface between the two solutions and wind the thread onto the glass rod.

Note

Nylon is a condensation polymer made up of repeating units of alternate hexane–1,6–diamine and dodecanedioyl units joined together by the elimination of hydrogen chloride to form a peptide link:

$$H_2N\text{---}(CH_2)_6\text{---}NH_2 \quad + \quad COCl\text{---}(CH_2)_8\text{---}COCl$$

$$\downarrow \; -HCl$$

$$\text{---}N\text{---}(CH_2)_6\text{---}N\text{---}C\text{---}(CH_2)_8\text{---}C\text{---}N\text{---}$$

15.7.2 Production of rayon

Copper(II) sulfate(VI) ($CuSO_4.5H_2O$)
Sodium carbonate (Na_2CO_3)
Concentrated ammonia solution
   (s.g. 0.88)
Sulfuric(VI) acid ($1\,mol\,dm^{-3}$)
Distilled water
Filter paper
Scissors
Plastic hypodermic syringe ($2\,cm^3$)

Glass rod, two beakers ($250\,cm^3$)
Beaker ($100\,cm^3$)
Top-pan balance
Spatula
Measuring cylinder ($100\,cm^3$)
Buchner funnel and flask
Water vacuum pump
Access to fume cupboard
Eye protection

Safety Copper(II) sulfate(VI) is harmful. Ammonia solution is corrosive and the vapour is toxic and can cause asthma attacks in susceptible people. The preparation of the solution should be carried out in a fume cupboard. $1\,mol\,dm^{-3}$ sulfuric(VI) acid is irritant. Because of the prevalence of drug abuse, syringes must be kept under close control.

Method

1. Dissolve 20 g of copper(II) sulfate(VI) in $100\,cm^3$ of distilled water.

2. Dissolve 4 g of sodium carbonate in $20\,cm^3$ of distilled water.

3. Mix the two solutions and filter using the Buchner funnel and flask connected to the water vacuum pump.

4. Wash the precipitated basic copper carbonate ($Cu(OH)_2/CuCO_3$) with distilled water, transfer it to a $250\,cm^3$ beaker and add $100\,cm^3$ of concentrated ammonia solution.

5. Stir to dissolve and then decant the resulting dark blue solution, which contains $[Cu(NH_3)_4]^{2+}$ ions, into the other beaker.

6. Using scissors, finely shred some filter paper.

7. Weigh out 2 g of shredded filter paper and stir this into the dark blue solution until it is completely dissolved, to produce a viscous liquid.

8. Withdraw some of this solution with the hypodermic syringe and slowly extrude it into a beaker containing sulfuric(VI) acid.

Sample results

A blue fibre of rayon formed which turned white on contact with the sulfuric(VI) acid.

Notes

1. The filter paper took about an hour to dissolve so it is advisable to have this already prepared.

2. A finer fibre can be obtained by fitting a hypodermic needle to the syringe. However, it will take more effort to extrude the solution from the syringe because of the solution's high viscosity.

4. Rayon is also known as viscose, so named because of the viscosity of solution which is extruded.

5. Rayon is a reconstituted cellulose fibre which contains about 300 glucose units per molecule (cf natural cellulose which contains between 2 000 and 10 000 glucose units per molecule).

15.7.3 Production of polyurethane foam

Polymer A (See note 1. below)   Glass rod
Polymer B (See note 1. below)   Eye protection
Plastic drinks cup   Access to fume cupboard
Measuring cylinder ($10\,cm^3$)

Safety This demonstration must be done in a fume cupboard because the vapour produced is toxic.

Method

Mix $10\,cm^3$ of polymer A with $10\,cm^3$ of polymer B in the plastic drinks cup and stir the mixture with the glass rod.

Sample results

After a few minutes an expanded polyurethane foam is produced which hardens in about 10 minutes.

Notes

1. The two ingredients are already partially polymerised so that toxic di-isocyanates are not present. However the monomers involved in the polymerisation are:

   i) diphenylmethane di-isocyanate:
   $$O=C=N-C(C_6H_6)_2N=C=O$$

   ii) diaminoethane 4-polyol:
   $$N(OH)_2CH_2CH_2N(OH)_2$$

2. This reaction illustrates the polymeric link formed in the reaction:

$$R-N=C=O \ + \ HO-R' \ \longrightarrow \ R-N-C-O-R'$$

with the N bearing an H below and the C bearing a double-bonded O below.

3. The polymerisation reaction is exothermic and the heat generated vaporises low-boiling liquids which froth up the reacting mixture to create the foam.

4. Taylor Ltd., Wollaston, Northants., Tel: 01933 664275 supplies the polymers.

15.7.4 Production of phenolic resin (Bakelite)

Retort stand and clamp
Boiling tube
Phenol
Formalin (40% methanal in distilled water)
Sodium hydroxide solution (30%)
Spatula
Anti-bumping granules

Bunsen burner
Top-pan balance
Measuring cylinder (10 cm^3)
Teat pipette (dropper)
Cloth
Mortar and pestle
Access to fume cupboard
Safety goggles

Safety Formalin is toxic, corrosive and a category 3 carcinogen. Phenol is toxic and should be handled wearing protective gloves. Sodium hydroxide solution (30%) is corrosive. Safety goggles (not safety spectacles) must be worn. The demonstration must be carried out in a fume cupboard.

Method

1. Using the measuring cylinder, transfer 2 cm^3 of formalin to the boiling tube and add 1 g of phenol followed by 2 drops of sodium hydroxide solution.

2. Add a few anti-bumping granules.

3. Clamp the tube in a retort stand and point the mouth of the tube away from the operator.

4. Boil gently to evaporate the water from the formalin and continue heating until the mixture polymerises.

Sample results

The mixture slowly darkens and a purple viscous resin forms which solidifies to a hard brittle product.

Notes

1. The polymer can be removed from the tube by wrapping the tube in a cloth and breaking the tube using a mortar and pestle.

2. The polymerisation takes place in stages:

   (i) Substitution of hydrogen by methanal at position 1 of a phenol molecule:

   (ii) Condensation of the product with more phenol:

   (iii) Product reacts with more methanal:

   (iv) Condensation of product with more phenol:

(v) The OH group also activates position 4 and 6 of the aromatic ring so substitution by methanal also occurs here. Successive substitutions and condensations produce a network of phenol molecules cross-linked by CH_2 groups from positions 2, 4 and 6 of the aromatic ring.

15.7.5 Measuring the gel time for epoxy resin

Ciba-Geigy Araldite consisting of (manufacturer's details) rapid hardener (N(3–dimethyl aminopropyl)–1,3–propylene-diamine) and rapid resin (bis phenol A-epichlorohydrin epoxy resin, average molecular mass 700)

Copper/constantan thermocouple
Spot galvanometer
Wooden splint
Scrap paper
Sellotape
Disposable polythene gloves

Safety Keep the resin off your hands by wearing disposable polythene gloves.

Method

1. Set the spot galvanometer at zero on scale × 1.

2. Connect the thermocouple to the galvanometer with the copper wire connected to the negative terminal and the constantan wire connected to the positive terminal.

3. Mix equal lengths of resin and hardener on a piece of scrap paper using the wooden splint.

4. Immerse the joint of the thermocouple in the mixture and hold it in position with Sellotape.

5. Record the galvanometer reading every 30 seconds for 10 minutes.

6. Plot a line graph of time/minute on the x-axis and galvanometer reading on the y-axis.

7. Interpolate the heating and cooling parts of the graph and read off the time where the two lines meet.

Sample results

Time/minute	Galvonometer reading	Time/minute	Galvonometer reading
0	0	5.5	18.0
0.5	0.6	6.0	15.2
1.0	0.6	6.5	11.6
1.5	0.7	7.0	9.2
2.0	0.7	7.5	7.2
2.5	2.0	8.0	5.6
3.0	2.4	8.5	4.0
3.5	5.0	9.0	3.3
4.0	7.5	9.5	3.0
4.5	13.0	10.0	1.4
5.0	off scale		

Note

The gel time for the Araldite was 5 minutes.

15.7.6. Factors affecting the polymerisation of styrene

Styrene monomer (recommended name: phenylethane)
Benzoquinone (recommended name: cyclohexadiene–1,4–dione)
Nitrobenzene
Benzoyl peroxide (recommended name: di(benzenecarbonyl) peroxide)
Teat pipette (dropper)
Top-pan balance
Spatula
Four test-tubes with corks
Beaker ($250\,cm^3$)
Measuring cylinder ($10\,cm^3$)
Kettle
Thermometer
Stop-watch
Marker pen
Ruler
Disposable polythene gloves
Eye protection
Access to a fume cupboard

Safety Styrene monomer is harmful and flammable. Nitrobenzene is very toxic and must be handled wearing protective gloves. Benzoquinone is toxic and irritant. Benzoyl peroxide is safe to use but hazardous to store. It is an oxidising agent and must be kept wet at all times. If it dries out in storage then there is a danger of fire. The demonstration must be carried out in a fume cupboard. The use of benzoyl peroxide in schools is not covered by the usually adopted model (general) assessments. A special risk assessment would be necessary before using it.

Method

1. Weigh out 0.01 g of benzoquinone, and three lots of 0.5 g of benzoyl peroxide.

2. Using the measuring cylinder, transfer 10 cm^3 of styrene to each of four test-tubes.

3. Boil some water in the kettle and transfer it to the beaker. Immerse the tubes in the beaker of hot water.

4. Treat the styrene in the four test-tubes with additives as follows:

Tube	Treatment
1	None
2	0.01 g of benzoquinone + 0.5 g of benzoyl peroxide
3	4 drops of nitrobenzene + 0.5 g of benzoyl peroxide
4	0.5 g benzoyl peroxide

5. Close the tubes with corks and shake the tubes until all of the additives have dissolved.

6. Keep the tubes in hot water and maintain a temperature of 85 °C with further additions of hot water as required.

7. Using the marker pen, make two marks, 5 cm apart, on the teat pipette.

8. After 30 minutes withdraw a pipette-full of the contents of each tube in turn, remove the teat and quickly close the pipette with your finger. Remove your finger and measure the time for the liquid in the pipette to flow the 5 cm down the pipette.

Sample results

Additives	Flow time/s
None	4.8
0.01 g of benzoquinone + 0.5 g of benzoyl peroxide	4.9
4 drops of nitrobenzene + 0.5 g of benzoyl peroxide	21.7
0.5 g benzoyl peroxide	73.2

Notes

1. The longer the flow time the greater the viscosity, therefore the more advanced is the polymerisation of the styrene.

2. Styrene polymerises by an addition reaction which involves the formation of free radicals. The benzoyl peroxide initiates free radical formation. Substances which react with the free radicals and destroy them as soon as they are formed are called inhibitors. Benzoquinone is an inhibitor. Substances which compete with the monomer for the free radicals are called retardants. They are less reactive than inhibitors. Nitrobenzene is a retardant. Inhibitors prevent polymerisation taking place, retardants merely slow the process down. Inhibitors can be regarded as highly efficient retardants.

3. It is essential to use inhibitor-free styrene for this investigation. This can be obtained by shaking styrene monomer with aqueous 10% sodium hydroxide solution (CORROSIVE), wash well with distilled water and dry it over anhydrous sodium sulfate(VI).

16 METHODS OF PREPARATION OF GASES

This chapter gives details of the preparation of six gases.

16.1 Hydrogen

Sulfuric(VI) acid (1 mol dm^{-3})
Granulated zinc
Copper(II) sulfate(VI) (CuSO$_4$.5H$_2$O)
Spoon spatula
Measuring cylinder (25 cm^3)

Top-pan balance
Eye protection
Apparatus shown in Figure 16.1
Safety screens

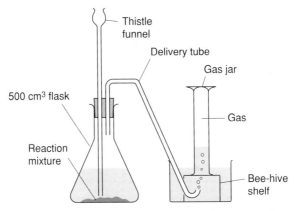

Figure 16.1 Collecting gases by downward displacement of water.

Safety 1 mol dm^{-3} sulfuric(VI) acid is irritant. Copper(II) sulfate(VI) is harmful. Hydrogen is extremely flammable and is explosive when mixed with oxygen. Hydrogen–air mixtures containing between 4% and 74% hydrogen by volume are explosive. Ensure that the stem of the thistle funnel is long enough to be immersed in the reaction mixture. Dismantle the apparatus and discard the reaction mixture by pouring it down the sink with plenty of water through a polythene funnel which separates any unreacted zinc granules.

Method
1. Set up the apparatus as shown in Figure 16.1 behind a safety screen.
2. Put between 2.5 and 5 g of zinc together with one flat spatula measure of copper(II) sulfate(VI) into the conical flask.

3. Add 25 cm^3 of sulfuric(VI) acid from the measuring cylinder down the thistle funnel and swirl the flask to mix.

4. Collect the gas by downward displacement of water as shown in Figure 16.1.

Notes

1. Sulfuric(VI) acid reacts with the zinc according to the equation:

$$Zn + H_2SO_4 \rightarrow ZnSO_4 + H_2$$

Copper(II) ions from the copper(II) sulfate(VI) catalyse the reaction.

2. The quantities of reactants suggested will provide two gas jars of hydrogen.

16.2 Carbon dioxide

Hydrochloric acid (1 mol dm^{-3})
Marble chippings
Spoon spatula
Measuring cylinder (50 cm^3)

Top-pan balance
Eye protection
Apparatus shown in Figure 16.1

Method

1. Set up the apparatus as shown in Figure 16.1.

2. Put between 2.5 and 5 g of marble chippings into the conical flask.

3. Add 50 cm^3 of hydrochloric acid from the measuring cylinder down the thistle funnel and swirl the flask to mix.

4. Collect the gas by downward displacement of water as shown in Figure 16.1.

Notes

1. Hydrochloric acid reacts with the calcium carbonate in the marble chippings according to the equation:

$$CaCO_3 + 2HCl \rightarrow CaCl_2 + H_2O + CO_2$$

2. The quantities of reactants suggested will provide two gas jars of carbon dioxide.

16.3 Oxygen

Hydrogen peroxide (10 vol)
Manganese(IV) oxide (manganese
   dioxide)
Spoon spatula

Measuring cylinder (50 cm^3)
Eye protection
Apparatus shown in Figure 16.1

Safety Risks are low with hydrogen peroxide at concentrations less than 18 vol. However manganese(IV) oxide is harmful. The oxygen produced is an oxidising agent.

Method

1. Set up the apparatus as shown in Figure 16.1.

2. Put three rounded spatula measures of manganese(VI) oxide into the conical flask.

3. Add 50 cm^3 of hydrogen peroxide from the measuring cylinder down the thistle funnel and swirl the flask to mix.

4. Collect the gas by downward displacement of water as shown in Figure 16.1.

Notes

1. Hydrogen peroxide catalytically decomposes in contact with manganese(VI) oxide according to the equation:

$$2H_2O_2 \rightarrow 2H_2O + O_2$$

2. The quantities of reactants suggested will provide two gas jars of gas.

16.4 Nitrogen monoxide

Copper turnings
Nitric(V) acid (50%)
Spoon spatula
Measuring cylinder (25 cm^3)
Eye protection

Apparatus shown in Figure 16.1 but
   using tap funnel instead of thistle
   funnel
Access to fume cupboard

Safety On exposure to air, nitrogen monoxide spontaneously oxidises to nitrogen dioxide which is very toxic. 50% nitric(V) acid is corrosive and an oxidising agent. This preparation must be done in a fume cupboard. Eye protection is essential.

Method

1. Set up the apparatus as shown in Figure 16.1.

2. Put three rounded spatula measures of copper turnings into the conical flask.

3. Add 15 cm^3 of nitric(V) acid from the measuring cylinder down the thistle funnel and swirl the flask to mix.

4. Collect the gas by downward displacement of water as shown in Figure 16.1.

Notes

1. Copper turnings react with 50% nitric(V) acid according to the following equation:

$$3Cu + 8HNO_3 \rightarrow 3Cu(NO_3)_2 + 4H_2O + 2NO$$

2. Soon after the addition of nitric(V) acid to the copper turnings, brown fumes of nitrogen dioxide are produced, partly by the action of the acid on the copper and partly by the nitrogen monoxide which is also formed reacting with oxygen in the air in the flask:

$$2NO + O_2 \rightarrow 2NO_2$$

Nitrogen monoxide is not very soluble in water. However, nitrogen dioxide is very soluble and dissolves in the water over which the nitrogen monoxide is collected.

3. The quantities of reactants suggested will provide two gas jars of gas.

16.5 Ammonia

Ammonium sulfate(VI)
Calcium hydroxide
Top-pan balance
Bunsen burner
Apparatus as shown in Figure 16.2

Red litmus paper
Forceps
Eye protection
Access to fume cupboard

Safety Ammonia is toxic by inhalation and can cause asthma attacks in susceptible people so make sure the room is well ventilated beforehand. The production of ammonia and filling the flask should be carried out in a fume cupboard. Eye protection is essential. Calcium oxide in the lime tower is corrosive.

Method

1. Set up the apparatus as shown in Figure 16.2 in a fume cupboard and put 1.8 g of ammonium sulfate(VI) together with 1 g of calcium hydroxide into the round-bottomed flask.

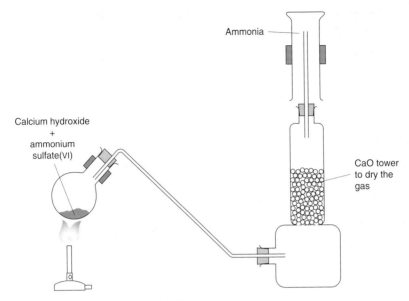

Figure 16.2 Preparation of ammonia.

2. Warm the flask with the Bunsen set on a non-luminous flame and then heat the flask more strongly.

3. Hold a piece of red litmus paper dampened with tap water in forceps and place it in the mouth of the inverted gas jar.

4. The gas jar contains sufficient ammonia for experiments when the litmus paper turns blue.

Notes

1. Ammonia is the only common alkaline gas and is detected by its ability to turn red litmus blue.

2. Ammonia is produced according to the equation:

$$(NH_4)_2SO_4 + Ca(OH)_2 \rightarrow CaSO_4 + 2H_2O + 2NH_3$$

3. Passing the ammonia through the lime tower removes the water from the gaseous mixture and produces a dry sample of ammonia:

$$CaO + H_2O \rightarrow Ca(OH)_2$$

4. The quantities of reactants suggested will provide two gas jars of gas.

16.6 Argon

Apparatus as shown in Figure 16.3   Eye protection
Six spent incandescent light bulbs

Safety **Risk of cuts from the broken glass from the light bulbs.
Dispose of the broken glass in a bin specially set aside for the
purpose.**

Note

Six light bulbs will provide sufficient argon to fill one gas jar.

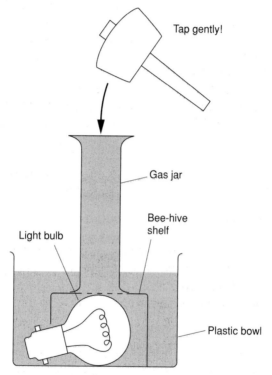

Figure 16.3 Argon from spent light bulbs.

17 QUALITATIVE CHEMICAL ANALYSIS

This chapter contains a collection of tests for a variety of substances.

17.1 Tests for common aqueous anions

Nitric(V) acid ($1\,mol\,dm^{-3}$)
  (CORROSIVE)
Hydrochloric acid ($1\,mol\,dm^{-3}$)
Sulfuric(VI) acid ($1\,mol\,dm^{-3}$)
  (IRRITANT)
Sodium carbonate solution
  ($1\,mol\,dm^{-3}$)
Sodium hydroxide solution
  ($1\,mol\,dm^{-3}$) (CORROSIVE)
Zinc powder (FLAMMABLE)
Ammonium molybdate solution
  ($0.5\,mol\,dm^{-3}$) (HARMFUL)
Spatula
Test-tubes
Red litmus paper
Filter paper and funnel
Barium chloride solution
  ($0.2\,mol\,dm^{-3}$) (TOXIC)

Silver nitrate(V) solution
  ($0.05\,mol\,dm^{-3}$)
Limewater (saturated calcium
  hydroxide solution)
Anti-bumping granules
Beaker ($100\,cm^3$)
Bunsen burner, tripod and gauze
Measuring cylinder ($50\,cm^3$)
Teat pipettes (droppers)
Eye protection
Calcium nitrate(V) (OXIDISING
  AGENT), potassium bromide,
  potassium iodide, sodium
  carbonate, iron(II) sulfate(VI)
  (HARMFUL), labelled A – F
  respectively

Safety All substances labelled as 'unknown' should be treated as hazardous. Eye protection is essential. The test for nitrate(V) must be carried out in a well ventilated area because the ammonia produced (if a nitrate(V) is present) is toxic. Warn asthmatics of the potential risks.

Method

1. Take each 'unknown' substance in turn and add one rounded spatula measure to $50\,cm^3$ of sodium carbonate solution in a $100\,cm^3$ beaker.

2. Add a pinch of anti-bumping granules and boil the mixture in order to precipitate any heavy metals.

3. Filter the mixture and divide the filtrate into four separate portions in test-tubes.

4. Carry out the following tests on the separate portions of filtrate:

   (i) Sulfate(VI): Add dilute HCl followed by $BaCl_2$ solution. A white precipitate of $BaSO_4$ is produced.

   (ii) Halide: Add dilute HNO3 followed by aqueous $AgNO_3$ solution. Off-white precipitate soluble in ammonia solution = chloride. Cream precipitate partially soluble in ammonia solution = bromide. Pale yellow precipitate insoluble in ammonia solution = iodide.

   (iii) Nitrate(V): Add zinc powder followed by NaOH solution and warm gently. Ammonia evolved which turns red litmus paper blue.

   (iv) Phosphate: Add ammonium molybdate solution followed by dilute nitric(V) acid and warm to about $60\,^\circ C$. A yellow precipitate is produced.

5. If the above tests are negative then the anion present is probably carbonate. Put approximately 1 g of the original substance into a test-tube and add a few drops of dilute nitric(V) acid. If the substance is a carbonate, carbon dioxide is evolved which turns limewater milky.

17.2 Tests for common aqueous cations

Sodium hydroxide solution
($1\,mol\,dm^{-3}$ and $4\,mol\,dm^{-3}$)
(CORROSIVE)
Hydrochloric acid ($1\,mol\,dm^{-3}$)
Aqueous ammonia ($1\,mol\,dm^{-3}$)
Concentrated ammonia solution
(s.g. 0.88) (CORROSIVE and produces a TOXIC GAS)
Red litmus paper
Forceps
Bunsen burner
Wooden splints
Test-tubes

Teat pipettes (droppers)
Eye protection
Solutions ($0.5\,mol\,dm^{-3}$) of the following substances labelled A–K respectively: Lead(II) nitrate(V) (TOXIC), aluminium sulfate(VI), zinc sulfate(VI), copper(II) sulfate(VI), iron(II) sulfate(VI), iron(III) chloride (IRRITANT), ammonium chloride, lithium chloride, sodium chloride, potassium chloride, barium chloride (TOXIC)

Safety All substances labelled as 'unknown' should be treated as hazardous. Eye protection is essential. The test for ammonia must be carried out in a well ventilated area because the ammonia produced (if ammonium ions are present) is toxic. Warn asthmatics of the potential risks. Pregnant women should not handle lead compounds because the effects are cumulative and there is the danger of damage to the unborn child.

Method

1. Using 2 cm^3 of each of the solutions labelled A–K in test-tubes, students attempt to identify the cations in the solutions using the key in Figure 17.1.

2. Carry out the flame tests by dipping a wooden splint in dilute HCl; then dip it into an aqueous solution of the cations and put it into a Bunsen burner flame.

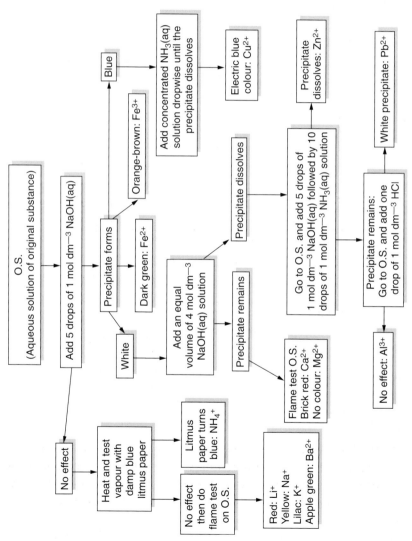

Figure 17.1 Key for identifying common aqueous cations.

253

17.3 Tests for common food-stuffs

Industrial methylated spirit
Distilled water
Sodium hydroxide solution
    (0.2 mol dm^{-3})
Copper(II) sulfate(VI)
Benedict's reagent (see Method 3)
Sulfuric(VI) acid (0.5 mol dm^{-3})
Gelatin
Sucrose

Glucose
Lard
Spatula
Test-tubes
Measuring cylinder (10 cm^3)
Beaker (250 cm^3)
Bunsen burner, tripod and gauze
Eye protection

Safety Industrial methylated spirit is highly flammable. 0.2 mol dm^{-3} sodium hydroxide solution is irritant. Copper(II) sulfate(VI) is harmful. 0.5 mol dm^{-3} sulfuric(VI) acid is irritant.

Method

1. Test the lard for the presence of fat by dissolving one spatula measure in industrial methylated spirit and then diluting with an equal volume of distilled water. The solution becomes turbid.

2. Suspend one spatula measure of gelatin in 5 cm^3 of distilled water and apply the Biuret test: Add 1 cm^3 of aqueous sodium hydroxide (0.2 mol dm^{-3}) to the suspension. Dissolve 0.25 g of $CuSO_4.5H_2O$ in 100 cm^3 of distilled water. Add one drop of this to the mixture. The Biuret test gives a violet colour.

3. Benedict's reagent is prepared by dissolving 100 g of sodium carbonate and 173 g of sodium citrate in 600 cm^3 of distilled water, filtering, and diluting to 850 cm^3. Dissolve 17.3 g of copper(II) sulfate(VI) in 150 cm^3 of distilled water and mix the two solutions.

4. Dissolve one spatula measure of glucose in 5 cm^3 of distilled water, add Benedict's solution and warm in a water bath. A red-brown precipitate is formed.

5. Repeat test 4 with sucrose in place of glucose. Benedict's test gives a negative result. Hydrolyse a fresh sucrose solution by boiling with an equal volume of sulfuric(VI) acid. Neutralise the solution by adding an equal volume of sodium hydroxide to the volume of sulfuric(VI) acid used for the hydrolysis and repeat Benedict's test. This time, Benedict's test gives a positive result.

17.4 Tests for reducing agents and oxidising agents

Acidified potassium manganate(VII) solution. Dissolve 4.3 g of potassium manganate(VII) in distilled water and add 10 cm^3 of 1 mol dm^{-3} sulfuric(VI) acid and dilute to 1 dm^3 with distilled water

Manganese(II) chloride

Concentrated hydrochloric acid

Spatula
Bunsen burner, tripod and gauze
Boiling tubes
Test-tubes
Teat pipettes
Top-pan balance
Eye protection

Safety 1 mol dm^{-3} sulfuric(VI) acid is irritant. Manganese(II) chloride is harmful. Concentrated hydrochloric acid is corrosive. Eye protection is essential when handling the solution of manganese(II) chloride in concentrated hydrochloric acid.

Method

1. Test suspected oxidising agents and reducing agents as follows:

   (i) Reducing agents: Add a few drops of acidified aqueous potassium manganate(VII) solution to 3 cm^3 of an aqueous solution of the reducing agent. The potassium manganate(VII) solution is decolorised by reducing agents.

   (ii) Oxidising agents: Dissolve 0.5 g of manganese(II) chloride in 5 cm^3 of concentrated hydrochloric acid, in a boiling tube. Add 0.5 g of the substance and boil. The solution will darken if the substance is an oxidising agent.

17.5 Diagnosis of illness by testing urine

Artificial urine samples prepared by adding two drops of yellow food colouring to 500 cm^3 of water to produce a suitable colour and then add: *Healthy*: nil. *Diabetic*: 1 g of glucose/100 cm^3 of urine. *Kidney disease*: 0.5 g of albumin/100 cm^3 of urine. *Jaundiced*: add 2 cm^3 of washing-up liquid/100 cm^3 of urine

Spatula
Sulfur
Clinistix and Albustix beads obtained from: Bayer Diagnostics, Evans House, Hamilton Close, Basingstoke, Hants, RG21 2YE
Eye protection

Safety Sulfur is flammable and produces a toxic gas when burned.

Method

Test the urine samples as follows:

(i) *Jaundice*: Add a spatula measure (0.2 g) of sulfur to 5 cm^3 of urine. The sulfur slowly sinks in jaundiced urine whereas it floats on the surface of healthy urine.

(ii) *Diabetes*: Dip a Clinistix bead into the urine. Diabetic urine changes the colour of the bead from pink to dark blue.

(iii) *Kidney disease*: Dip an Albustix bead into the urine. The urine changes the colour of the bead from pale yellow to dark yellow-green.